THE MACMILLAN READING PROGRAM

Senior Authors

Albert J. Harris

Mae Knight Clark

ENCHANTED GATES

A book is an enchanted gate,

That leads to magic lands,

But cross the threshold and your fate

A poet's pen commands.

"A Book Is an Enchanted Gate," *by Morris Abel Beer*

Josephine L. Wright

ENCHANTED GATES

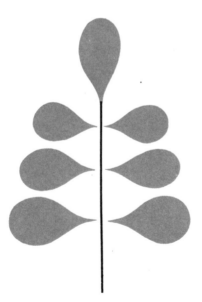

CALIFORNIA STATE SERIES
Published by
CALIFORNIA STATE DEPARTMENT OF EDUCATION
Sacramento, 1969

The Macmillan Company, New York
Collier-Macmillan Canada, Ltd., Toronto, Ontario
Printed in the United States of America

Illustrated by

Les Goldstein, Burt Groedel, Karel Kezer
George Porter, Ed Young

Grateful acknowledgment is made to the following authors and publishers for permission to use copyrighted material:

Abingdon Press, for "Spring Secret," copyright 1952 by Pierce & Smith, from *Winds A'Blowing*, by permission of Abingdon Press; for "Friends," from *Winds A'Blowing*, copyright © 1961 by Abingdon Press; for "Wobbly Wheels," adapted from *Wobbly Wheels* by Lilian Moore, copyright © 1956 by Pierce and Washabaugh. Used by permission of Abingdon Press, publishers.

Atheneum Publishers, for "Associations" (titled in this book "Home to Me Is Not a House"), from *There Is No Rhyme for Silver*, copyright © 1962 by Eve Merriam, used by permission of Atheneum Publishers; for "Quibble," from *There Is No Rhyme for Silver*, copyright © 1962 by Eve Merriam, used by permission of Atheneum Publishers.

The Bobbs-Merrill Company, Inc., for "Mr. Dawson and the Kite," adapted from *Mr. Dawson Had a Farm* by R. O. Work, copyright 1951 by The Bobbs-Merrill Company, Inc., reprinted by permission of the publishers.

Dodd, Mead & Company, for "Patrick's Dog," reprinted by permission of Dodd, Mead & Company, adapted from *Patrick Visits the Library* by Maureen Daly, copyright © 1961 by Maureen Daly.

Doubleday & Company, Inc., for "Could It Have Been a Shadow?", from *Goose Grass Rhymes* by Monica Shannon, copyright 1930 by Doubleday & Company, Inc., reprinted by permission of the publishers.

E. P. Dutton & Co., Inc., for "My Dog," copyright 1932, renewal © 1960 by Marchette Chute, from the book *Around and About* by Marchette Chute, published 1957 by E. P. Dutton & Co., Inc., and reprinted with their permission.

Aileen Fisher, for "Otherwise," from *Up the Windy Hill*, published by Abelard Press, 1953.

Harcourt, Brace & World, Inc., for "Wings and Wheels," from *Magpie Lane* by Nancy Byrd Turner, copyright 1927 by Harcourt, Brace & World, Inc., renewed 1955 by Nancy Byrd Turner, and reprinted by permission of the publishers.

Harper & Row, Publishers, Inc., for "Rubber Bones," an approved adaptation of "Rubber Bones," from *Let's Experiment* by Jacqueline Harris Straus, copyright © 1962 by Jacqueline Harris Straus.

Alfred A. Knopf, Inc., for "Three Cousins," adapted from *What's a Cousin?* by Helen D. Olds, by permission of Alfred A. Knopf, Inc., copyright 1962 by Helen D. Olds.

J. B. Lippincott Company, for three stanzas from "I Keep Three Wishes Ready," from *All Through the Year* by Annette Wynne, copyright 1932, 1959 by Annette Wynne, published by J. B. Lippincott Company.

Little, Brown and Company, for "Scat! Scitten!", from *Take Sky* by David McCord, copyright 1961, 1962 by David McCord, by permission of Little, Brown and Company; for "How Many Pennies?", adapted from "How Many Pennies?" by Louisa Rydberg, copyright 1954 by The Curtis Publishing Company, from *Jack and Jill 'Round the Year Book*, edited by Ada Campbell Rose, by permission of Little, Brown and Company; for "The Hot Weather Mix-Up," adapted from "The Hot Weather Mix-Up" by Frances B. Watts, copyright © 1957 by The Curtis Publishing Company, from *Jack and Jill 'Round the Year Book*, edited by Ada Campbell Rose, by permission of Little, Brown and Company.

The Macmillan Company, for "A Tiger in the Cherry Tree," adapted from *A Tiger in the Cherry Tree* by Glen Dines, © The Macmillan Company 1958, and used with their permission.

McGraw-Hill Book Company, Inc., for "The Little Whistler," with permission of McGraw-Hill Book Company/Whittlesey House, from *The Little Whistler* by Frances Frost, copyright © 1949 by McGraw-Hill Book Company.

William Morrow and Company, Inc., for "The Snowstorm," an adaptation of a chapter from *Snowbound with Betsy* by Carolyn Haywood, copyright © 1962 by Carolyn Haywood, by permission of William Morrow and Company, Inc.

G. P. Putnam's Sons, for "Rain," from *Everything and Anything* by Dorothy Aldis, copyright 1925, 1926, 1927 by Dorothy Aldis, reprinted by permission of G. P. Putnam's Sons; originally published by Minton, Balch and Co.

Franklin Watts, Inc., for "The Boy Called Booie," adapted from *Somebody Called Booie* by Lillian Gardner, published by Franklin Watts, Inc., © 1955.

Contents

They Try Again

Finding Out

Anything Can Happen

Thinking of Others

They Try Again

Mrs. Hardy's Cat

"Hello, Mrs. Hardy," said Kay.
"Are you going to ride to your new house
in the truck?"

"No, I can walk to it," said Mrs. Hardy.

"I can take the cat for you," said Andy.
"I like cats."

"Can't the cat walk, too?" asked Kay.

Mrs. Hardy said, "She can walk,
but it will be good to have Andy take her.
That dog down the street runs after her
when he sees her."

"I want to go with Andy," said Kay.

"Good!" said Mrs. Hardy. "I have
something new that I want to show
both of you. I must hurry now.
You can see it when you come
with the cat."

Mrs. Hardy went back into the house
to get her things. She wanted to take them
with her.

"Let's tell Mother about it," said Kay.
"I know she will want us to take the cat
for Mrs. Hardy. Get the cat, Andy."

Andy got the cat, and they went
next door to their house. They went
around to the back door.

As they went in, the cat jumped down
and ran. Andy ran after her.

When Andy tried to catch the cat,
he fell.

"Andy!" said his mother. "Are you hurt?"

"No, Mother," said Andy, getting up.

"Just look at what you did!"
his mother said. "What are you two doing
with Mrs. Hardy's cat?"

"Mrs. Hardy wants us to take the cat
to her new house," said Kay. "We will help
you first, Mother."

Andy and Kay helped their mother.
Then they looked around for the cat.
She was not there, so they went
to look for her.

Andy Gets the Cat

"There she is!" said Andy. "I'll get her."

"Don't go out there, Andy!" said Kay. "You may fall! Mother won't like it!"

Andy said, "I won't fall. I have to get the cat, don't I?" He went out after the cat.

Andy did fall. As he fell, the cat was in his way. Down she went, too.

15

Andy fell into a tree by the house.
As he went down he felt something catch
in the seat of his pants.

The next thing Andy knew, he was hanging
from the tree. He couldn't get down,
and he couldn't get up again.

Kay was yelling, "Help! Help!"
Mrs. Hardy came out of her door.

"Andy!" called Mrs. Hardy. "What
on earth are you doing hanging in that tree?"

"He was trying to get the cat," said Kay.
"He fell."

The men who had Mrs. Hardy's things
in their truck heard Kay yelling. They saw
Andy hanging in the tree. They came to help
and soon got him down.

"Just look at your pants!" said Mrs. Hardy.
"I'll fix them for you, but I can't do it now.
I must go on over and tell the men
where to put things. Where is the cat?"

"I don't know, but I'll find her,"
said Andy. "Then we will hurry right over."

"All right," said Mrs. Hardy. "I must go
on to the new house. I'll be there
when you come with the cat. I'll fix
your pants then."

Andy said, "Ask Mother for a sack, Kay.
We will put the cat into a sack. Then I
can take her on my bike. We can go
to the new house in a hurry."

Kay got a white sack, and they put
the cat into it. It was an old sack
with holes in it. Andy said that was
all right. "The holes in the sack
will let the cat get air," he said.

Andy took the cat on his bike.
Kay got her bike and went with him.

The Cat and the Sack

Soon the cat had two feet out of the sack.
Then the hole got so big that all four feet
were out. She jumped off the bike.

People on the street stopped to look.
There was a white sack running
down the street! It was running
on four feet. A boy and a girl
were after it!

The cat couldn't see where she was going.
She ran into a man, and down went
his packages. Andy and Kay stopped
to help him.

Soon the man had all his things again.
Then the children looked for the cat.
She had run away again.

"Now what?" asked Kay.

"I'll find her," said Andy. "Just see
if I don't. Let's take the bikes back
and then look for her."

As they were putting their bikes away,
something said, "Meow! Meow!"

There was the cat at Mrs. Hardy's door.
She had come back home.

"Meow! Meow!" she said again.

"She wants something," said Kay.
"Let's fix her something to eat."

They got something for the cat to eat,
but she didn't eat it. She went over
to Andy. She looked up at him and said,
"Meow! Meow!"

She said it again and again.

"I don't know what she wants,"
said Andy.

"She may be scared," said Kay.
"Let's take her to Mrs. Hardy."

21

Andy took the cat, and they went
to Mrs. Hardy's new house. This time
they walked.

On the way Kay said, "Let me
take her now, Andy. I like to hold her."

"I do, too," said Andy. "I like cats."
He petted the cat a little. Then he let Kay
take her.

Kay said, "I want a cat, but not a big one.
I want a little kitten to love and pet."

"I do, too, but will we ever get one?"
asked Andy.

When they got to Mrs. Hardy's house,
Kay put the cat down. The cat ran
to Mrs. Hardy and said, "Meow! Meow!"

Kay said, "She wants something. We
don't know what it is. We tried to give her
something to eat, but she didn't eat it."

Mrs. Hardy laughed. "I know what she
wants," she said. "Come with me and see
what will happen. Then I'll fix Andy's pants."

She took Kay and Andy to see
four new baby kittens! The mother cat ran
to her kittens. How happy they were
to see each other.

Three of the kittens were black and
white. One was yellow like the mother cat.

"I want you to have one of the kittens,"
said Mrs. Hardy. "You may take it home soon.
It is not big enough now to stay away
from its mother.

"I asked your mother about it and she said
you could have one. Do you want the yellow
one, or one of the others?"

"Oh!" Kay and Andy said together.
"The yellow one!"

"The yellow one it is," said Mrs. Hardy.

Wobbly Wheels

Jenny sat up in bed. "It may be today!"
she said. "It may happen today."

She jumped out of bed and ran
to look outside. "Maybe now," she said.
"Maybe when I look out now, I'll see
that it has happened."

She looked outside. No, not a thing
had happened. The rain had not stopped.

"Rain! Rain! Rain! Will it ever
go away?" asked Jenny.

Jenny's mother came to the door.

"Oh, Mother! Is that rain ever
going to stop?" asked Jenny.

Her mother said, "I know, Jenny.
It's too bad that it rains day after day.
I know you want to ride your new bike.
The news says that the rain may stop soon.
Then you can ride."

Jenny ran to look at her new red bike—
her first two-wheeler!

"I have had it for six days now,"
she said. "Six days, and I have not
had a ride on my two-wheeler."

When Jenny got to school that morning, she saw Pete. Pete lived down the street from Jenny's house. She knew that he wanted the rain to stop. She knew why, too. Pete had new skates.

Pete had told Jenny about his skates. "They are new and bright," he had said. "The wheels zip around like anything."

Now Pete said to Jenny, "Won't this rain ever stop? I want to try out my new skates."

"Mother says it will stop soon," said Jenny. "She heard it on the TV news."

It Happened Next Morning

When Jenny looked out the next morning
the rain had stopped.

She had to take time to eat.
Then she asked, "Mother, may I take
my bike out now? The rain has stopped,
and you said I could. May I?"

"I can't take time to help you right now,"
said her mother.

"Please, Mother!" said Jenny.
"Let me go out now. I'll be careful.
I'll stay on our sidewalk."

Her mother said, "Oh, all right!
If you will stay on our sidewalk.
You must know how to ride before you go
into the street. Please be careful."

Jenny ran and got her bike.
She wheeled it out to the sidewalk.
She was careful not to let her dress
catch on a pedal.

She put one foot on a pedal and
sat on the seat. She tried putting
the other foot on a pedal. The bike fell
over on its side.

Riding a bike didn't look hard
when other people did it. They just
got on their bikes and went riding away.
That was not the way it happened
with Jenny. When she put her feet
on the pedals, the bike fell.
Over it went on its side.

First it went to one side. Then it went
to the other.

Jenny walked around to the other side
of the bike. She tried getting on that way.
Over went the bike again. She couldn't
stay on long enough to make it go.

"This bike is wobbly," said Jenny.
"Something about it is not right."

Jenny took hold of the bike again.
As soon as she put her feet on the pedals,
over it went.

Jenny put the bike by the wall
of the house. Then she sat down.
She wanted to cry.

"Old wobbly wheels!" she said
to the new red bike. "You are no good!"

Helping Each Other

Jenny saw Pete coming. He had
his new skates, but he was not skating.
He didn't look happy.

"Hello, Pete!" said Jenny. "Let me see
your new skates."

Pete said, "They are no good. The wheels
are wobbly. I can't make my skates go
where I want them to go. One foot
goes this way. One foot goes that way.
Then I sit down hard."

"Oh, it's like that at first,"
said Jenny. "You have to keep on trying."

"I did keep on," said Pete. "I tried
a long time. The wheels are too wobbly."

"Your skates look all right to me,"
said Jenny. "Put them on. Let me see
what they do."

Pete put the skates on and got up.
One skate went that way. One skate went
this way. Pete sat down hard.

"See what happens?" he asked.

"Yes, Pete," said Jenny.
"But you are not doing it right."

She helped him to his feet. "Hold on
to me, Pete. Let me show you. Your skates
are all right. If you keep on trying,
you will soon know how to skate."

Pete held on to Jenny and tried
again and again. Up and down the sidewalk
they went. Up and down, up and down.

At last Pete said, "Say!
This is all right! I can skate!"
He was skating without Jenny's help.

Just then he saw Jenny's bike.
"That's a good bike!" he said.
"How does it ride?"

"I can't ride it," said Jenny.
"It won't stay up! It's too wobbly.
Daddy is coming home soon. Maybe
he can fix it."

Pete took off his skates and
tried Jenny's bike.

"This bike is all right," he said.
"Get on. I'll hold it for you so it
will stay up."

Jenny got on the bike. It began
to go over, but Pete held on. It didn't
go down this time.

"Now, Jenny," said Pete. "The right pedal
is up as high as it will go. Push down on it
as hard as you can."

Jenny tried.

"Harder!" said Pete. "Try it again,
and push down harder on the pedal."

Pete held the bike, and Jenny tried again.

"That's it," yelled Pete. "Now
the other foot. Come on, Jenny! Push down
on it harder! Keep both feet going."

Jenny felt the wheels go round.

"Now do that again," said Pete.
"This time, don't stop. I'll hold on."

Up and down the sidewalk they went.
Jenny worked hard to make the wheels
go round. She tried again and again.

Jenny's mother looked out the door.
There was Jenny, riding up and down
the sidewalk on her two-wheeler!
Pete was skating by her side.

They laughed together as Pete called,
"Our wheels are not wobbly now!"

Rain

Raining again
And raining again,
Freckles of rain on the
Window pane,
Pricks in the puddles
As bright as a pin
Stop and begin and then
Stop and begin:

John flats his nose on the
Window pane,
Watching and watching and
Watching the rain!
John can't remember
He's ever been
Any place but
Always in.

Dorothy Aldis

Wings and Wheels

Ahoy and ahoy, birds!
We cannot have wings
And feathers and things,
But dashing on wheels
With the wind at our heels
Is almost like flying—
Such joy, birds!

Oho and oho, birds!
Of course we can't rise
Up and up to the skies;
But skimming and sliding
On rollers, and gliding,
Is almost as jolly,
You know, birds!

Nancy Byrd Turner

Hound-Pup's Big Ears

Hound-Pup was a very little pup.
There was one big thing about him.
It was his ears. His ears looked
very big on a pup that was so little.

Hound-Pup's father and mother liked
his big ears. So did all his friends.
All the cats on the street liked them.
The rabbits liked them, too.

"Oh, my, yes!" said the mother rabbit.
"I like your ears. They are long like ours."

"I don't like them," said Hound-Pup.
"I don't care who likes my long ears.
They get in my way."

One day one of the kittens wanted
to play with Hound-Pup. "You are **It**,
Hound-Pup! You are **It**!" she called.

Hound-Pup ran after her and tried
to catch her. He fell over one of his ears.
Over and over he went!

He got up and tried again to catch
the kitten. It was hard for him to run.
His ears were in his way.

A blue jay flew by. "Ack! Ack!"
the blue jay called. "Be careful Hound-Pup.
Hold your ears up or you won't get there!"

Hound-Pup couldn't hold his ears up.
He just walked away and went to bed.
He couldn't eat his dinner.

The next day the kitten said, "Hound-Pup! You didn't eat your dinner, and you don't look very happy. Why don't you come out and play?"

"It's my ears," said Hound-Pup. "They are so big! Every time I try to run I fall over them. I don't know what to do."

"Here," said the kitten. "Let me fix them for you." She took hold of his ears and tied them together.

"There!" she said. "They are out of your way now."

"Let's play," said Hound-Pup. So they ran and played and had fun. Hound-Pup didn't fall over his ears at all.

Just then Mrs. Cat came by. "Just look
at Hound-Pup!" she said. "With his ears
tied together, he looks like a little toy dog!"

Hound-Pup sat down hard. He didn't like
to be called a little toy dog.

"I can't have my ears tied together
like this," he said. "I won't be a little
toy dog! I'll just go back to my doghouse
and stay there!"

Now Hound-Pup was unhappy again. He
was so unhappy that he couldn't eat his dinner.

The next day the kitten said,
"How about this? Let me tie up an ear
on each side. Maybe that will help."

She tied his ears up again. This time
she tied up one ear on each side.

"Now your ears don't look big,"
said the kitten.

"Let's ask Jack Rabbit about that,"
said Hound-Pup.

They called Jack Rabbit. When he saw
Hound-Pup, he laughed. He laughed so hard
he couldn't stop.

"I just can't look at you without laughing,"
he said. "Go look at yourself."

Hound-Pup was so unhappy that he ran
to his doghouse. He saw his dinner
in his dish, but he couldn't eat it. He went
into his doghouse and didn't come out.

Old Red Helps

One day Old Red came by. He was
the oldest dog on the farm. He saw
Hound-Pup looking unhappy.

"Sit down, my boy, and tell me all
about it," he said.

Hound-Pup told Old Red all about his ears.

"Please," asked Hound-Pup. "Is there
anything I can do?"

"Yes, there is," said Old Red.
"Go home now. Every day after dinner,
look at yourself in a bright, shiny dish.
When you see yourself in the shiny dish,
bark three times. Do this every day,
but don't tell."

When Hound-Pup got home, his sister
asked, "Why are you looking so happy?"

"I can't tell you," said Hound-Pup.
"It's a secret. I'll tell you just one thing.
My ears are not going to be so big."

"How do you know?" she asked.

"That's the secret," said Hound-Pup.

Hound-Pup said to himself, "I must have
a bright, shiny dish. Oh, I know!
My dinner dish!"

Hound-Pup had to eat all his dinner.
Then he could see himself in the dish.
When he saw himself, he barked three times.

Every day Hound-Pup did what Old Red
had told him to do. First he had his dinner.
Then he looked at himself in the dish.
When he saw himself, he barked three times.
Each day he said to himself,
"I **must** have small ears!"
By and by he saw that his ears
did look smaller. How happy he was!

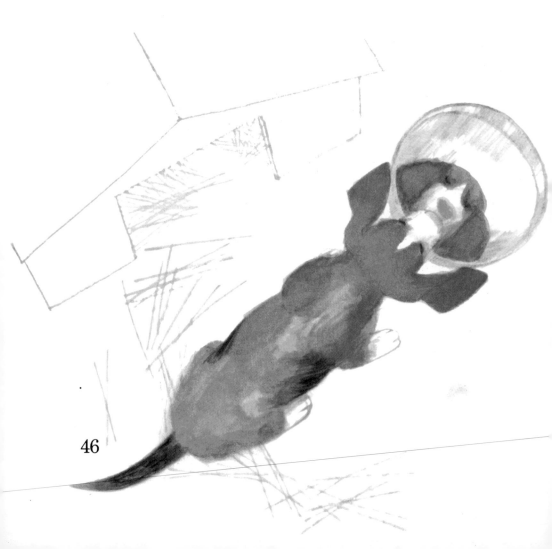

One Saturday the oldest dog came by.
"Look here, Old Red!" called Hound-Pup.
"The secret worked! My ears
are getting smaller."

Old Red laughed. "No," he said.
"They are not smaller."

"Oh, yes," said Hound-Pup.
"They are not so long now. I don't fall
over them."

"I know," said Old Red. "That's because
you are bigger. Your ears are bigger, too.
They just don't look as big."

"Why—that's right," said Hound-Pup.

"It's because **I** am bigger! Tell me,
please! How did looking in my dish and
barking make me bigger?"

"Looking in your dish every day
didn't make you bigger," said Old Red.
"Eating your dinner every day did that."

"What about the barking?" asked Hound-
Pup. "How did that help?"

"A hound dog has to know how to bark,"
said Old Red. "You don't bark like a pup, now.
You bark like a hound dog."

Hound-Pup was very, very happy.
"May I tell the secret now?" he asked.

"Yes," said Old Red. "Run home and tell
all of them. Tell them you are not
a hound pup. You are a hound dog now."

How Many Pennies?

It was Timmy's birthday. His father said,
"Timmy! You are old enough now
to have money of your own. From now on,
you will get ten pennies each Saturday.
You may do as you like with them."

Timmy's father took the money
out of his pocket. Then he counted
ten shiny new pennies for Timmy.

Timmy knew that his big brother and sister
got more money each Saturday. That was
all right with him. They got just ten pennies
when they were as old as Timmy.

Timmy showed his pennies
to his brother Dick. Then he put them
back into his pocket.

"Don't keep your pennies in your pocket
like that," said Dick. "That's not
a good thing to do."

"Where do you keep your money?"
Timmy asked.

Dick put his hand into the pocket
of his pants. He took out his pocketbook.
He held it out and showed it to Timmy.
"I keep my money in a pocketbook," he said.

Timmy said, "I can't do that because
I don't have a pocketbook."

Timmy put his pennies into a small sack.

Timmy showed his pennies
to his sister Nan. "Where do you keep
your money?" he asked.

"In my little bank," said his sister.
She showed Timmy the little bank
where she put her money.

"I don't have a little bank,"
said Timmy. He went to find his mother.

"Mother, I have to keep my pennies
in this sack," said Timmy. "I don't have
a pocketbook, and I don't have a bank."

"I'll fix a bank for you,"
said Timmy's mother. "Get me a pint jar."
She took the pint jar and cut a hole
in the top. "There," she said. "A pint jar
will make a good bank."

"Thank you, Mother," said Timmy.
He took his pennies out of the sack.
He put them into the bank. He liked
the noise of the pennies as they fell
into the jar.

"Mother," said Timmy. "How many
pennies will it take to fill this jar?"

His mother laughed. "I don't know,"
she said.

Timmy Keeps On Trying

Timmy went to his father.

"Daddy, see my bank?" he said.

"How many pennies will it take to fill it?"

"I don't know," his father said.

"It will take many, many pennies."

Timmy asked Nan and Dick, but they didn't know.

"I will ask my teacher," he said.

At school the next day, Timmy told
his teacher about the pennies.
"How many will it take to fill a pint jar,
Mrs. White?" he asked.

"I don't know," she said.

Timmy and Nan walked home together.
"I asked Mrs. White about the pennies,"
he said. "She didn't know how many
it would take to fill my bank."

"I know how we can find out," Nan said.
"We can go to the library. The librarian
will look it up for you." So Nan took Timmy
to a library that was close by.

"This is my brother Timmy," Nan said to the librarian. "He wants you to find something for him."

"Good morning, Timmy," said the librarian. "How can I help you?"

"How many pennies will it take to fill a pint jar?" asked Timmy.

"You stay here. I'll be right back," the librarian said. She didn't come back for a long time. When she came back, she said, "I can't help you after all. We can't find the answer."

"I will find out some way," said Timmy. "I'll keep on trying until I do."

Timmy Finds Out

Timmy asked Dick what to do next.

Dick said, "Go to the bank. If you want
to know about money, ask a banker.
A banker knows all about money."

One day soon, Dick took Timmy
to the bank. The two boys walked over
to a man who was working there.

"Hello, boys!" said the man. "Can I do
something for you?"

"Yes, thank you," Dick answered.
"This is my brother Timmy. He wants
to ask you something about money."

The man looked at Timmy.

"How many pennies will it take to fill a pint jar?" Timmy asked.

"To fill a pint jar!" said the man. "I don't know. I don't know at all. Let me see if I can find out."

When he came back he said, "I can't help you. No one here knows the answer."

On the way home Dick said, "Find out for yourself, Timmy."

"Could I?" asked Timmy. "How?"

"Just keep putting pennies into your jar. When it will not hold one more, count the pennies. It will take a long time, but it's one way to find out."

"That's just what I'll do!" said Timmy.
"I'll find out for myself."

Every Saturday Timmy put two or three
of his pennies into the jar. Some Saturdays
Nan and Dick put some of their pennies in, too.

Now and then their father looked over
his money. He put some pennies
from his pocket into Timmy's bank.
Mother helped, too. She put in some
of her pennies. The jar began to fill up.

The days went by. Now and then Timmy
counted his pennies. Each time there were
many more. One day he counted one hundred
pennies. The next time he counted, he had
two hundred ten.

A long time went by, and it was Timmy's birthday again. He counted his pennies. There were three hundred five. He said, "I began putting pennies into this jar on my last birthday. Now my birthday is here again, and the jar is not filled!"

More people began to help Timmy. At last, not one more penny would go in.

Dick said, "Let's all count them now!"

"No!" said Timmy. "I want to count them all by myself."

"Yes," said his mother, "I know you do. You count them. Then you can tell us how many pennies it took to fill the jar."

Timmy took the top off the jar. He put
all the pennies on his bed. Then he began
to count. He put the pennies back into the jar
as he counted. As he put the last one in,
Timmy laughed. He said to himself, "Maybe
I know something that no one knows but me.
I know how many pennies it takes to fill
a pint jar. I won't keep it a secret."

He jumped off the bed. Then he ran
to tell his mother and the others.

The next day, he told his teacher.
One day he told the librarian and the people
at the bank. Now he wants **you** to know.
It took six hundred sixty-nine pennies
to fill the pint jar.

What Did Danny Do?

"Mother," said Danny, "will you give me
two dollars?"

"Why do you want two dollars?"
his mother asked.

"I want to finish my airplane,"
answered Danny. "I'll have to hurry.
I want it finished for the school fair.
I must have a pint of red paint and
some other things. Then I can finish it."

"Oh, Danny!" said his mother.
"I do want to help you, but I can't give you
two dollars now."

"Saturday?" asked Danny.

"No," she said. "It may be a long time
before I can give it to you."

Danny didn't say anything more. He knew that his mother would help him if she could.

Danny went to look at his airplane. He liked the way it looked. He had worked very hard on it.

"If I can just finish it in time!" he said to himself. "I may get the prize. I told my teacher I would have it ready. I must think of some way to get two dollars myself. It's just ten days until the fair."

Danny was out on the sidewalk thinking about his airplane. He saw Sam Story coming down the street.

As Sam went by, Danny said, "Hello, Sam! What's your hurry?"

"Got to get a friend to take over my work,"
said Sam. "I'm going away. Going to be away
eight days."

Danny knew about Sam's work.
Sam was taking care of Mrs. Green's dog.
She was away, so every day Sam had
to walk her dog. He had to give it something
to eat, too.

"Let me do it, Sam," said Danny.
"I'll take good care of the dog."

"Oh, I don't know about that," said Sam.

"Please, Sam," said Danny. "I want
two dollars. I must have money to finish
my airplane for the fair. What will I get
if I take care of the dog for you?"

"All of it," said Sam. "That's just what
I would get for eight days—two dollars.
But I don't know. You are so little, Danny."

"I'm not little," said Danny. "I'm seven,
going on eight. Let me do it, Sam. Please!"

"I'll see about it," said Sam.
"You may not like it after you try it.
You may want to stop before I get back.
Maybe Frank Kakai will take it over
if you do. If he says he will,
I'll let you try it."

"Good!" said Danny. "I know that I
won't want to stop, but let's go see Frank."

64

The boys went to Frank's apartment.

Frank Kakai said, "Yes. If Danny wants
to stop, he can let me know. I'll take care
of the dog. I'll see that he's all right, Sam."

The very next day, Danny began
to take care of the dog. He liked dogs,
so it was not hard work.

One day went by. Then two and three
and four. On the next day Danny came in
from walking the dog. His best friend,
Jay, was at his apartment.

"Good news, Danny!" said Jay.
"My dad is going fishing for three days.
He says you and I can go with him."

"Say!" said Danny. "That **is** good news!
May I go, Mother?   Please!"

"What about Mrs. Green's dog?"
asked his mother.

"Oh, Mother! I don't want to stay home
because of the dog," Danny answered.
"Frank Kakai will take care of him.
He said he would if I wanted him to."

Then Danny began to think about his
airplane. He did want to finish it and take it
to the fair. But he wanted to go fishing, too.
What should he do?

What do **you** think he did?

Consonants and Vowels

Consonant letters are not hard to know,
  They say what they have to say.
Most of them have only one kind of sound,
  But some are said more than one way.

C is a letter without its own sound,
  You say it like **s** or like **k**:
S when in **city** and **k** when in **cat**,
  And getting it right is like play.

Some other consonants sound in two ways,
  As all of you know they may do;
But look out for vowels! It's hard to know all
  The sounds of **a, e, i, o, u**!

Mae Knight Clark

The Little Whistler

My mother whistled softly,
My father whistled bravely,
My brother whistled merrily,
And I tried all day long!
I blew my breath inwards,
I blew my breath outwards,
But all you heard was breath blowing
And not a bit of song!

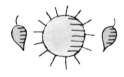

But today I heard a bluebird,
A happy, young, and new bird,
Whistling in the apple tree—
He'd just discovered how!
Then quick I blew my breath in,
And gay I blew my breath out,
And sudden I blew three wild notes—
And I can whistle now!

Frances Frost

Miss Baker

Space Monkey

Finding Out

The Surprise Cake

"I must go now," said Mrs. Hall.
"I'll come back as soon as I can."

Betty said, "We will be all right, Mother.
I'll look after things."

"Yes," said Mrs. Hall. "I know you will,
and the other children can help you. See that
the goats don't get out of the barn, Betty.
A man is coming for them Saturday."

"Please come back soon," said Joy.

"I will," said Mrs. Hall. "Chet, don't try
to make anything new until I get back.
I like to be at home when you try out
new things."

Chet answered, "All right, Mother."
He was always trying out something new.
Not everything came out right. Sometimes
things that happened were a big surprise,
but they were fun to try.

73

After Mrs. Hall got on the bus,
the children went back into the house.

"I know what I'm going to do," said Betty.
"I'm going to make a cake. It will be
a surprise for Mother when she gets back.
You two go out and play."

Betty got out the cookbook.

"I want to help," said Chet.

"No, you are too little," said Betty.

"I am not!" said Chet. "That's what
you always say. I'm six. I'll be seven
on my next birthday."

Joy said, "We want to help. We want
to surprise Mother, too."

"You can help by staying out of my way,"
said Betty. "Go play until I call you."

Joy and Chet didn't like that,
but they went out to play.

74

Soon Chet came running back to the house.
He opened the door and called, "Betty, Betty!
The goats are out of the barn. I'm going
to get them."

"No, you are not," said Betty.
"You stay here with Joy. I'll get them
back into the barn."

Before Chet could say anything more,
Betty was running after the goats.
Soon she and the goats were out of sight.

75

Chet and the Cookbook

"I know what I'll do," said Chet.
"I'll make the cake. We can surprise Mother
after all."

Joy said, "You can't make a cake. Didn't
Mother tell you not to make anything new?"

"Cake isn't new," said Chet. "We
have had cake more times than you can count.
This cookbook tells how to make cake."

"Can you read it?" asked Joy.

"Yes, I can read it," said Chet.
"I'll soon be seven."

"You won't be seven very soon," said Joy.

Chet looked at the cookbook and
began to read. He said, "It says 'CAKES'
right here. White Cake. Yellow Cake.
I'll make a yellow cake."

Joy said, "You **can** read, can't you?"

"That's right," said Chet. "Get some eggs,
Joy. The book says, 'Beat four eggs
until light.' I'll get the egg beater."

Joy got the eggs. Chet put four of them
into a bowl. He began to beat them.

Chet said, "Now, let's see. The cookbook
says to beat one cup of something
with the eggs. I can't tell what it is.
It says, '. . . one cup of s-u-g-a-r.' "

"Isn't it sugar?" asked Joy.
"Mother always puts sugar in a cake."

"That's it," said Chet. "I'll get
the sugar." Then he said, "Here's the sugar."
He put one cup of it into the bowl.
He began to beat it with the eggs.

"Put the sugar back where it was, Joy,"
he said.

Just then Betty came back.

"I had a time with the goats," she said.
"I got them back into the barn at last."

Then she said, "Chet!
What are you doing?"

"Making the cake," said Chet.
"I put in the eggs and sugar."
He looked at the cookbook and said,
"Please help me read this, Betty."

"Let me have the bowl," said Betty.
"I'll do it."

Chet said, "It's my cake."

"We will make it together," said Betty.
"The surprise will be from all of us."

"Oh, all right," said Chet. He didn't know
what to do next, anyway.

Betty soon got the cake ready to bake.

When Mrs. Hall came home, the cake
was ready. It didn't look right, but
Mrs. Hall was pleased with the surprise.

"Let's eat some of it right now,"
she said. She put away a package
that she had with her. Then she cut
the cake and gave some to each of them.

Chet took a big bite and yelled.

Joy had tried hers, too. "It's bad,
bad cake," she cried.

Their mother tried a very little bite.
"I know what you did," she said. "I'll
show you."

Mrs. Hall said, "Look at this, Chet.
Is this what you put into the cake for sugar?"

"I know now!" Chet cried. "That's salt.
It's not sugar!"

His mother said, "You will soon know
how to read well, Chet. Then you won't do
that kind of thing. We must not be unhappy
about the cake. It showed you how important
one word can be."

Then she said, "I have a surprise for you. When I saw your cake, I put my surprise away for another time. I'll get it now."

She got the package that she had put away. "Here's my surprise," she said. She opened it and took out—a cake!

Ben Franklin

Ben Franklin was a real boy. He lived
a long time ago.

One day Ben was walking down the street.
He felt in his pocket. Yes, his pennies were
there—all ten of them.

Ben knew there were ten pennies. He
had counted them over and over.
He didn't get many pennies.

Ben looked down the street and
saw his friend Pat. As Pat came up to Ben,
he blew and blew on a whistle.

"Hello!" said Ben. "I like that whistle. May I try it?"

"No," said Pat. He blew on the whistle again and again.

"Sell it to me," said Ben. "I'll give you my pennies for it."

"What pennies?" asked Pat. "You don't have any pennies. Not real pennies."

"I do!" cried Ben. "I have ten real pennies." He took the pennies out of his pocket and counted them.

"They are real, all right," said Pat. "Where did you get them? Your father didn't give them to you, did he?"

"No," said Ben. "A friend of his gave them to me. I can use them any way I please."

"Here's the whistle," said Pat.
"I'll sell it to you for ten pennies."

Pat put the pennies in his pocket
and ran off in a hurry.

Ben began to blow the whistle.
He ran home to show it to his brothers
and sisters.

When he went inside, his father said,
"Ben! It's time to eat. Please stop making
that noise and get ready."

When they were all seated, Ben took out
his whistle. Everyone was looking at it.
He felt very important.

"Where did you get that?" asked one
of his brothers.

"From Pat," said Ben. "It's my whistle."

"Did you use one of your pennies
to get it?" asked a sister.

"Not just one!" said Ben. "This is
a good whistle."

Ben's father looked at the whistle. "You
can get a whistle like this for one penny,"
he said. "How many did you give him?"

Ben didn't want to say. He looked down
and didn't say anything.

His father asked again, "How many, Ben?
Tell me."

Ben couldn't look at his father. At last
he said, "All ten pennies, Father."

"That was too much," said Mr. Franklin.

Ben was not happy with his whistle now.
He jumped to his feet. "I'll find Pat
and get my pennies back," he cried.

Mr. Franklin said, "Sit down, Ben. I want
to tell you something important. When you
give something away, don't try to get it back.
Next time, take care not to give too much
for things."

"I will," said Ben. "After this I'll
find out about things first. I'll be careful
not to give too much for anything again."

Ben Wants to Know

When Ben Franklin was bigger, he always wanted to know about things. He was always asking his father and brothers, "What?" and "How?" and "Why?"

They couldn't always tell him what he wanted to know. When they couldn't tell him, Ben tried to find out for himself.

Many times Ben **did** find out things that no one knew before. The other boys would say, "That Ben Franklin! He's always finding out something new!"

Ben lived close to the water. He liked to go there to see the boats. He saw how the wind blew them across the water.

One day Ben said to himself, "Why can't
the wind help me float across the water?
I know something I'm going to try."

Ben got his big kite. He took hold
of the kite string and ran with it.
The wind took the kite up into the air.
Then Ben jumped into the water.

The wind blew the kite high into the air.
Ben began to float across the water.
Soon he was on the other side, and he had not
worked at all. The wind and the kite did
the work.

One boy yelled, "Look at Ben floating
across the water! His kite is taking him
to the other side without any work!"

"Yes," said another. "He's always finding
new ways to do things!"

When Ben was a man, he didn't stop trying to do new things. People felt that some of the things he did were magic. They talked about this man who was always making important new things. Now they began to call him "Benjamin"—not just "Ben." Benjamin Franklin was his real name.

At that time there was no TV. There were no airplanes and no rockets. Many things you have now were not made then.

People of that day knew very little about electricity. They didn't have anything run by electricity as we have now. Benjamin Franklin knew as much about electricity as other people did. He wanted to find out more.

At that time men knew how to make some electricity. They used a kind of jar. When the jar was rubbed, it made electricity. It had to be rubbed with silk to make electricity.

Franklin had one of the jars. He and his friends liked to experiment with it. They wanted to use the jar to find out more about electricity. They knew people could get hurt by electricity. But there was not enough of it in this jar to hurt them.

They couldn't use the electricity, because they didn't know enough about it.

"There must be some way that men can use electricity," said Franklin. He went right on doing experiments with it.

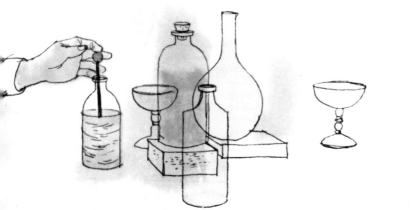

Franklin's Experiment

Benjamin Franklin had looked at lightning many times. He had said to himself, "I think lightning must be electricity. I'm going to try to find out. I know an experiment I can try."

Franklin made a big silk kite and put a string on it. He tied a key to the string. Then he tied a silk string to the key.

He said to his helper, "The electricity will not come down the silk string. The key will get the electricity and hold it. If we put the jar close to the key, the electricity will go into the jar. We can keep it to use in other experiments."

Soon the rain and lightning came again. Benjamin Franklin flew the kite up very high.

The kite string got wet, and lightning
came down it to the key.

A spark came from the key and
hurt his hand. Now Franklin knew
that lightning was electricity.

Franklin had a jar ready. Now he told
his helper to hold it up close to the key.

The electricity from the lightning went
into the jar. Benjamin Franklin took the jar
home. He put a wire from it to a small bell.
The electricity in the jar made the bell ring.

"We did it!" cried Franklin. "We have
used electricity from lightning."

Benjamin Franklin worked and worked
to find out more about electricity. The work
that he did helped people find ways
to use electricity.

Now we use electricity in many, many ways. We use it for lights. We use it to run the TV. We use it to run many other things. It would be hard to name all of them. Benjamin Franklin helped us to have them.

People said, "Franklin was always asking, 'How?' and 'What?' and 'Why?' Then he would find out the answers for himself."

He tried other experiments. He made many new things that people could use.

You can read about Benjamin Franklin in other books. Some of them tell about his important experiments.

The Magic Show

David worked hard at school, and all
the children liked him. He was a happy boy
most of the time.

Sometimes he felt unhappy when he saw
the other boys playing. He would think
to himself, "I wish I could do **something** well.
I can't run or do the high jump. I wish——"
But wishing didn't help.

One morning David was looking
at the others play. He was wishing his wish
as one of the girls came up.

"David," said Sue, "I want to talk to you
about our next Hobby Time. Five of us
had to plan our next show at school. We know
what we are going to do. We are going
to have a magic show."

"A magic show!" said David. "We can't do
any magic."

"Oh, it won't be real magic," Sue answered.
"It will just be make-believe. We can do
any trick that the others don't know about.
It will look like magic because they
won't know how to do it."

"Oh, I see," said David. Then he looked
away. "I can't do any tricks. How can I?"

"Why, David!" cried Sue. "You may do
the best one of all. There are all kinds
of tricks. You read so well, David.
Your hobby is reading. Maybe you can find
a good trick in a book."

"Yes, I can!" cried David. "I know
just the right book. It isn't really
about magic. It's a book about experiments.
Some of the experiments make things happen
like magic. I know the very page I want."

David smiled and said, "I'll be ready
for the magic show, Sue. I really will.
Thanks for telling me about it."

That morning, the teacher asked Sue
to tell about the plans for Hobby Time.
The children liked the magic show plan.

"Let's vote for the best magic trick
in the show," said one boy.

"Yes!" said the others. They all wanted
to vote.

The children began to think
about the show. Each one wanted
to have the best trick.

"I'm going to do a trick with a rope,"
one boy said. "I saw a cowboy do it on TV."

"I'll make a fish float in the air,"
said a girl. "It can float on a wire
too small to be seen."

"You told!" cried Sue. "Now it won't be
like magic."

"Oh!" said the girl, looking very unhappy.
"Now I can't use that trick! I'll have to think
of another one."

David went to the library and got the book that he wanted. It was about experiments. He looked up the page he wanted to read.

"Mother," he said. "I want a wishbone. Do you know where I can get the wishbone from a chicken? The bone must not have a crack in it."

"A wishbone!" said his mother. "Yes, we are going to have chicken for dinner. You may have the wishbone. What will you do with it?"

"Use it for an experiment," David said. "I want some vinegar, too. May I have a little vinegar?"

"Yes," answered his mother. "But what **can** you do with vinegar and a wishbone?"

David smiled and answered, "Make the bone look like rubber."

Hobby Day

The day for the Magic Show came. The children who had magic tricks to show took turns doing them. Some of the tricks were very good.

When David's turn came, he held up the wishbone. "Do you know what this is?" he asked.

"Yes!" the children answered. "It's a wishbone."

"That's right," said David. "We had chicken for dinner, and Mother gave me the wishbone. I have a note from my mother. It tells that this bone was really taken from a chicken."

David gave the note to his teacher and
she read:

> This is to say that the wishbone
> David will show you is a real bone.
> It was taken from a chicken
> that we had for dinner.
>
> David's Mother

The teacher finished reading the note.
David held the wishbone up again.

"Now I'll say some magic words,"
he said. "When I finish, this wishbone
will be turned to rubber."

David held the wishbone in one hand.
He used his other hand to cover it. He said,

"Shish! Shish! Dee, dee, dee!
Turn to rubber, bone, for me."

"Now," said David, opening his hands.
"The wishbone has turned to rubber! It's
not hard, as bone is. See how soft it is.
I can bend it like this."

He showed the children that the bone
was as soft as rubber. He handed the bone
to one of the children. Yes, it was as soft
as a rubber bone. The children handed it
from one to another. Each one wanted
to bend the soft bone.

It really did look like rubber. It felt
like rubber, too. They didn't know what
to think.

"How did you do it?" they cried. David
smiled but didn't tell.

The time came to vote for the best trick. The wishbone magic got more votes than any of them.

"I wish David would tell us how he did it," said Sue.

David laughed. "All right," he said. "I'll tell you how."

He did tell them.

If you want to know, too, you can find out. The experiment that David used for his trick is on the next page. It is taken from the book of experiments that David read.

Turn the page and read it.

Rubber Bones

To do this experiment you will need three things:

> 1 wishbone from a chicken
> Some vinegar
> A small jar or dish

Be careful to see that the wishbone has no little cracks in it. If it does have cracks, the experiment will not work well.

Put the wishbone into the jar or dish. Cover it with vinegar. Let it stay in the jar all night.

The next morning, take the wishbone out of the jar. It will be like rubber. It will be very soft and you can bend it.

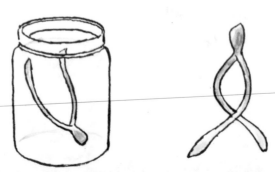

Patrick's Dog

"What I want for my birthday can't be put into a package," said Patrick.

"Is it a ride in an airplane?" asked his father.

Patrick answered, "No, not that."

"Your own rocket?" asked his mother.

"No, not a rocket," said Patrick.

"Is it a ride to the moon?" asked his sister Maria.

Patrick laughed. "Not one of you is right," he said. "What I want more than anything is a dog."

"A dog!" said Maria.

"A dog all my own," said Patrick.

Patrick's father said, "A dog must have good care. It must be taken out to walk every day. Someone must play with it, too."

"Someone must give it water and something to eat every day," said his mother.

"Someone must teach a dog to stay off the streets," said his father. "Then cars or trucks won't run over it."

"A dog must have somewhere to sleep," said his mother. "It must have someone to love it. Someone must teach it to be a good dog."

"That's why!" said Patrick. "All the things you have said tell why I want a dog!"

"Patrick is big enough to take care
of a dog," said his father. "What kind
of dog do you want, Patrick?"

"I don't know," Patrick said. "I saw
a big brown and white dog on Mr. Black's
farm. I liked that one."

"That's a good dog for the farm,"
said his father. "It is big, and it can help
the farmer with his work. It's just right
for the farm. I think it's much too big
for our apartment."

"I know the little dog that lives
next door," said Patrick. "I like
its color, but I don't see it play much.
It sleeps too much for me."

"It's right for the people who own it,"
said Patrick's mother. "That dog makes
very little noise. They are old people,
so they like that kind of dog."

"Oh, I know!" said Patrick. "How about
that big black dog? The one that rides
in the car with the policeman. Now **there's**
a dog I like!"

"I like it, too," said his father.
"But that's a kind of dog that works
with policemen. It can catch people who
run away from the policemen. It's
a brave dog. It will fight hard when that
is what the policemen want. It is a good dog
for policemen. Do we need a policeman's dog?"

"No, I don't think we do," said Patrick. "Each kind of dog I know about is right for someone. Not one is just right for me. There must be **one** dog that's right for me. I don't know which one that will be. I just don't know enough about dogs."

His mother said, "I know what you can do, Patrick. You have enough time before your birthday to find out about dogs. You can go to the library."

"To the library!" cried Maria. "Are there dogs in the library?"

"No!" Patrick's mother laughed. "There are books in the library. Books about dogs. Books to help Patrick find out which kind of dog he wants."

Patrick at the Library

After school the next day, Patrick
and his mother went to the library.
When they got there, they went
into the children's room.

The room was big and bright, with many,
many books. Patrick had never seen
so many books!

Patrick's mother told the librarian
her name. Then she said, "This is Patrick.
He wants to learn about dogs."

"We have many books about dogs,"
said the librarian. "We have books
on most things a boy wants to know."

The librarian went over to one wall
of books. "See here, Patrick," she said.
"All the books on this wall are about dogs.
Some of them tell about the kinds of dogs
there are. Some tell how to take care
of a dog. Some tell how to help a dog
learn tricks. Others tell how to teach him
to do whatever he is told.

"There are some that just have good stories
about dogs. Look them over and find some
you like. If you need help, let me know."

Patrick's mother said, "I'll go into the next room. I want to look for a book I need. You can look at dog books."

Patrick looked at the books. He found two that he liked.

One of the books was about the many kinds of dogs. The other one had good dog stories in it. Patrick liked both of the books.

He liked to look around the library, too. Other children were looking at books. Patrick counted ten boys and six girls in the room.

112

Soon Patrick's mother came back and said, "We must go now, Patrick."

Patrick said, "Oh, Mother! I'm not ready to go. I want to look at the books some more. I don't know enough about dogs yet."

"You can come back tomorrow," said his mother. "We will ask for a library card for you. After you get a card, you can take books home with you."

"Oh, boy!" said Patrick. "I have found just the book I want to take home!"

Patrick told the librarian that he wanted
a library card. "Mother is in a hurry now,"
he said. "I will bring the card back
when I come tomorrow. I want it so that
I can take library books home. I have found
one that I want to read."

"That's good," said the librarian.
"We will take care of that right away.
You can write your name, can't you?"

"Oh, yes," Patrick answered. "I can write
just about anything."

"Can you write your address?"
asked the librarian.

"Yes," said Patrick. "My address tells
where I live. I can write that, all right."

"Take this card," said the librarian.
"Write your name and address on it. Ask
your mother to write her name on the back.
Then give it to me when you come tomorrow.
We will get your library card ready
for you. Then you can take books home
with you. You can take two at a time."

"Is that all there is to do?" asked Patrick.
"I want to learn all about dogs. After that
I want to read stories about outer space."

"There is one thing more to do,"
said the librarian. "The books are
for all the children who want them.
We must all help take care of them."

Patrick and the librarian talked
about ways to take care of books.
Then she said, "Come back soon, Patrick."

The Right Dog

After that, Patrick got book after book from the library. He learned many things about dogs. There was one thing he didn't know yet. He didn't know what kind of dog he would choose. His birthday was coming very soon.

"I know about many kinds of dogs now," said Patrick to his mother. "I like them **all**!"

"Don't you know yet which one you like best?" asked Maria.

"No," said Patrick. "I like one kind because it's big and can take care of me. I like another kind because it's little and can learn tricks well. I like the big black-and-white ones because they look so good. And I like another kind because of their red color."

"You can't have four dogs!" said Maria. "You can have only one!"

"He won't have one dog if he can't choose the one he wants," said their mother.

"I know it," said Patrick. "I **must** choose the right dog for me. I know one thing—I want a real tail wagger."

"There's not much time," said his mother. "Your birthday is next Saturday."

One night Patrick said, "I need to get another dog book."

His mother laughed. "I think this is a dog house now," she said. "All we talk about is dogs, dogs, dogs!"

His father said, "You won't have time to get another book. Tomorrow is Saturday. We are going to the pet shop, Patrick. You can try to choose one you really want. If you find him, he will be your birthday dog."

"I'll choose one," said Patrick. To himself he kept saying, "What if I don't choose the right one?"

118

Patrick got up the next morning as soon as it was day. He wanted to be ready to go to the pet shop.

When they got there, his father said, "Take your time. You have read about all kinds of dogs. Now walk around and look at them."

There were many kinds of dogs in the shop. There were big ones, little ones, and dogs of many colors.

"Oh!" Patrick said. "What dog do I want?"

Patrick walked and walked, and looked and looked. At last he came to a little white dog with one black spot. Patrick stopped and looked at him.

"Why, he smiled at me," said Patrick.

Then Patrick said, "Hello, Spot!"

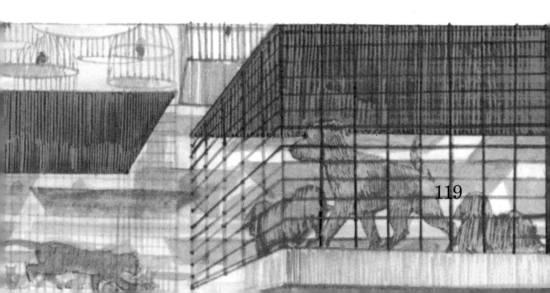

The little dog wagged his tail and tried
to get to Patrick. Then he did a little trick.
He looked at Patrick and wagged his tail
again and again.

"Look at this one, Dad!" said Patrick.
"Spot likes me! He wants me to play with him.
He's doing tricks to make me look at him."

Patrick's father smiled. "Why do you
call him Spot?" he asked.

"I named him Spot," said Patrick.
"That must be because he's my dog.
I **do** want him, Dad."

"All right," said Patrick's father,
"if you think he is the one."

"I know he is," said Patrick.

Patrick and his father went home,
with Patrick holding Spot.

"Oh, Patrick, I like him!" said Maria.
"How did you happen to pick this one?"

"I don't know why I picked this one,"
answered Patrick. "Spot must have some way
to find out about boys. I didn't pick a dog
after all. My dog picked me. He's
a real tail wagger."

121

My Dog

His nose is short and scrubby;
  His ears hang rather low;
And he always brings the stick back,
  No matter how far you throw.

He gets spanked rather often
  For things he shouldn't do,
Like lying-on-beds, and barking,
  And eating up shoes when they're new.

He always wants to be going
  Where he isn't supposed to go.
He tracks up the house when it's snowing—
  Oh puppy, I love you so!

Marchette Chute

Miss Baker

Miss Baker was a real monkey. She was very little. She didn't weigh as much as a big kitten. You could have held her in one hand.

She was always jumping up on people or things, and running around. She liked to have fun.

Miss Baker was a bright little monkey. She knew many tricks, but she was not a pet. She was a very important monkey. That's because she went into outer space before men did.

At that time people didn't know much
about outer space. Men had sent rockets
into outer space, but they had never sent
a man.

Men said, "We don't know enough
about outer space yet. We must know more
about it. A man can't go up in a rocket
until we do."

Many men were working together.
They knew some things about outer space.
They wanted to find out much more.

The men talked together. One man said,
"I think a monkey should go up next.
A monkey is very like a man. Let's see
if a monkey can go up and come back all right.
If it does, maybe a man can do it, too."

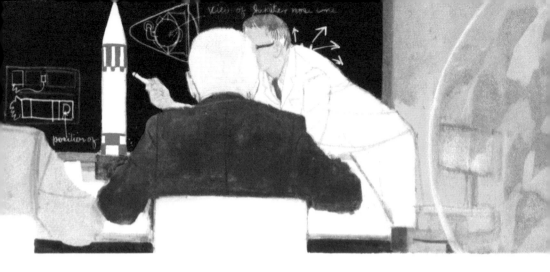

"Yes," said another. "Let's try
a monkey next. We must be very careful.
First we must teach the monkey to ride
in a rocket."

"That's right," said another. "We must
find just the right monkey, too. It must be one
that can learn the things it needs to know."

"Let's send up two kinds," a man said.
"Let's send a small kind of monkey and
a bigger kind." So that was the plan.

The Navy men were to teach a small kind
of monkey. The Army men were to teach
a bigger kind. They each planned to teach
many monkeys. Then they would choose
the best ones for the rocket ride. They
would send up only one of each kind.

125

Mr. West took care of the monkeys
that were sent to the Navy. Many others
helped him.

The monkeys were put into cages.
Mr. West went to look at them.
The little monkeys were afraid of Mr. West.
When he came to a cage, they ran
to the other side. They didn't want
to be close to him.

The smallest monkey of all looked
at Mr. West. She came over to the side
of her cage. Then she put out her small hand.
Mr. West took it in his.

He took the little monkey out of the cage
and petted her. "I see we are going
to be friends," he said. "You are the only one
that isn't afraid."

That monkey was little Miss Baker.
She didn't have that name then. She was just
one of the little monkeys. All of them
would learn to ride in a rocket. One of them
would be picked to go into outer space.

At first the monkeys were afraid
of the rocket. The men petted
the monkeys and gave them good things
to eat. They learned to like the men.
Little by little they stopped being afraid
of the rocket.

The monkeys learned to do just as they
were told. They learned to stay in the rocket
longer and longer. They learned to ride
upside down. They could go without eating
for a day and a night.

Some of the monkeys didn't learn well, but many did. Little Miss Baker was one of the best. Others were good, too. It was hard for the men to choose.

The time came for the rocket to go into outer space. The Navy men asked a doctor to choose the monkey to ride in it.

The doctor saw the monkeys do all the things they had learned. Many of them did well! He didn't know what to say.

One little monkey looked up at the doctor. She put out her hand.

"Oh," said the doctor. "So you want to be the one to go! All right. You did very well, so we will send you."

Mr. West smiled. The doctor had picked his little friend, Miss Baker!

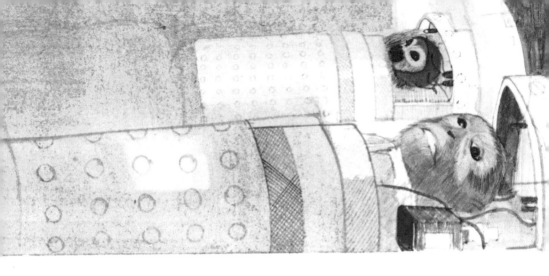

The Rocket Ride

The big day came. The men took
Miss Baker to the rocket. There she saw
the monkey that was to go with her. It was
the first time she had seen this monkey.
Its name was Able.

Able and Miss Baker were put
into the nose cone of a rocket. They
were not afraid. They did just what
they had learned to do.

The time for the countdown came. Ten,
nine, eight, seven, six, five, four, three,
two, one, zero! There was a big, big noise and
a very bright light. The blast-off had come!
The rocket was up and away!

129

The men looked up at the rocket as long
as they could see it. They knew that it
would go far up into outer space. There
the nose cone would come off the rocket.
It would fall back to earth with the monkeys
in it! Would they be alive?

If the nose cone came down right,
it would fall into the water. Then
men would hurry to get it. Some
Navy ships were far out on the water.
Men on one of them were ready to get
the nose cone.

Airplanes with big lights on them
flew over the water. The lights were to help
the men see the nose cone when it came down.

The men on the ships saw the nose cone
come down. It fell into the water. Then
the men couldn't see it. They looked and
looked for it. At last a man yelled,
"There it is! The nose cone! There it is
on the water!"

Four men from the ship went to it
in a hurry. Two of them jumped
into the water to help get the nose cone.
It was hard for them to get hold of it
but they did. They fixed it so that it
could be pulled up.

Soon the nose cone was on the ship.
Men went to work on it to get it open.
Would the monkeys be alive after that long,
hard ride into space? No one knew.

One doctor was ready to take care of Able.
Another was ready to take care of Baker.

131

When the men got the nose cone open,
both monkeys were alive. The doctors
looked them over. "The monkeys
are all right," they said. "Give them
something to eat."

That was just what the monkeys wanted!

The two monkeys were not hurt at all
by going into outer space. Now a man
could try it.

Soon a man did try it, but Able and Baker
had gone first!

The two monkeys were sent back
to their homes.

Mr. West smiled when he saw Miss Baker.
He said, "My, but it's good to see you!
I'm so glad that you came back all right!"

Some people wanted to give prizes
to the space monkeys. Able didn't live
long enough to get a prize, but Miss Baker did!

Many people came to see the little monkey
get her prize. She took her prize and
looked at it. Then she tried to eat it!
She couldn't do that, so she put it on.

Miss Baker didn't know why the prize
was so important. She didn't know that she
and Able were our first astronauts.

Spring Secret

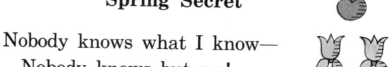

Nobody knows what I know—
  Nobody knows but me!
I hunted around and around about
To find the secret, and found it out.
Nobody knows what I know,
  Nobody knows but me!

Nobody knows what I know,
  Nobody knows but me!
It's high-up-high in an apple tree,
And snug and safe as a nest can be.
Nobody knows what we know—
  The mother bird and me!

May Justus

Z-Words

Not many words begin with **Z,**
That buzzes like an angry bee.

Yet if there were no **Z,** could you
Find a **zebra** in the **zoo?**

Without the countdown **zero,** when
Would **zooming** rocket flights begin?

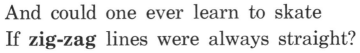

And could one ever learn to skate
If **zig-zag** lines were always straight?

Yes, z-words can be very handy,
For **zippers** in our clothes are dandy!

Mae Knight Clark

Anything Can Happen

Mr. Dawson and the Kite

One day Mrs. Dawson was talking
to Mr. Dawson. "I want to put some jars away
in the cellar," she said. "Will you please
clean it today? I don't want to put anything
more in the cellar until it is cleaned."

"All right," said Mr. Dawson. "I'll
clean it, but first I must take this rope
to Mr. Long. I'll clean the cellar
when I get back."

Mr. Dawson went to take the rope
to Mr. Long. On the way back he saw one
of the Shaw boys with a kite.

"Hello!" said Mr. Dawson. "I flew kites
when I was a boy. I like to fly kites."

138

"Many men like to fly kites,"
said Robert Shaw. "Benjamin Franklin
flew a kite. I read about it at school.
He put a key on his kite string."

"A key?" said Mr. Dawson.
"Why did he do that?"

"He found out something, but I have
forgotten what," said Robert. "I would
put a key on my kite if I had one.
I don't have any keys."

"Now what did he find out? I just
can't think what it was," said Mr. Dawson.
"Robert, we have a key to lock our cellar door.
We can put that key on your kite. Maybe we
can find out what Benjamin Franklin did!"

"I don't know," said Robert.
"We can try."

Robert got his kite down. Then he and
Mr. Dawson went to get the key.

When they got to the Dawson cellar,
the key was in the door.

"Someone locked the door and didn't take
the key out," said Mr. Dawson. "I'll turn
the key in the lock before I take it out.
Mrs. Dawson may want to get into the cellar."

Mr. Dawson tied the cellar key on Robert's kite string. Then Robert ran with the kite.

"There she goes, Mr. Dawson!" cried Robert. "Look at her fly! She's really getting up there."

"Let me hold the string," said Mr. Dawson.

"Well, all right," said Robert. "Don't let out too much string."

Robert gave him the string. Mr. Dawson let the string out just a little at a time. The kite went higher and higher in the air.

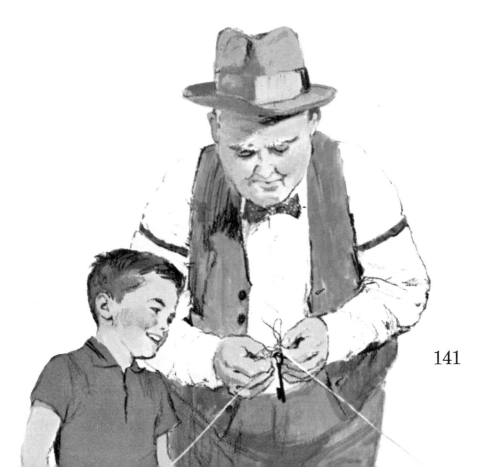

"It's so high you can't see the key now,"
said Robert. "I can't think what's going
to happen to it. I wish I had not forgotten
what happened to Benjamin Franklin's key."

Just then Robert's mother called him.
"Aw!" he said. "Mother wants me right now.
It will take a long time to get this kite down."

"You run on, Robert," said Mr. Dawson.
"I'll get your kite down for you."

Robert went on home. Mr. Dawson began
to take in the kite. He was pulling it down
when he dropped the string. The wind blew
the kite high in the air. Mr. Dawson tried
to get hold of the string again. It was
so high that he couldn't catch it.

"Oh, dear," thought Mr. Dawson.
"I wish I had not dropped that string.
What if the kite goes into the trees!"
   That is just what the kite did.
It dropped into a very tall tree.
   "My word!" thought Mr. Dawson,
when he saw the kite in the tree.
"How am I going to get the kite down?
I can't go up that tall tree. Maybe
I can make another kite for Robert."

Who Is Knocking?

Mr. Dawson went home. When
he got there, he looked everywhere
for his wife. He couldn't find her.
"Where can she be?" he thought.
"I'll call Mrs. Long."

He called the Longs' house. "Hello,
Mrs. Long," he said. "I can't find my wife.
Is she at your house?"

Just then he heard a knock
at the back door. "Please hold on,"
he said to Mrs. Long. "Someone is knocking
at my back door."

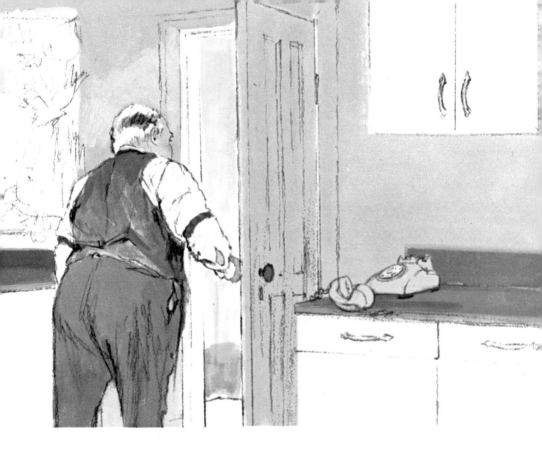

When he went to the door, no one
was there. "That's funny," he said.

He went back to finish talking
to Mrs. Long.

"Is my wife there, Mrs. Long?" he asked.

"No," said Mrs. Long. "I have not seen her
all day. Did you telephone Mrs. Banks?"

"No," said Mr. Dawson. "I'll call her
right now."

Mr. Dawson called Mrs. Banks. Just as Mrs. Banks answered, he said, "Please hold on, Mrs. Banks. I hear someone knocking at my back door. I answered it once and there was no one there."

Again he went to the door, but no one was there. He went back to the telephone and talked to Mrs. Banks.

"I haven't seen your wife today," said Mrs. Banks. "Have you tried calling the Blacks?"

Mr. Dawson called the Blacks. She was not there.

She was not at the Halls'. She was not at Mrs. Hardy's.

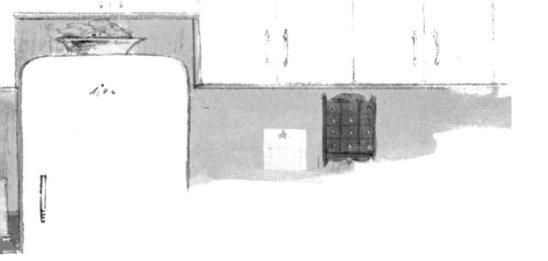

He heard the knocking once more. There
was no one at the door when he answered it.

"She must be at the Littles'," said
Mr. Dawson. "I'll call there. Oh, dear!
I hear that knocking again." No one was
at the door, so he called Mrs. Little.

"No," Mrs. Little answered.
"I haven't seen your wife once today.
What could have happened to her?"

"I don't know," said Mr. Dawson.
"Something very funny is going on here.
Someone keeps knocking at my back door.
I have answered it four times,
but no one is there."

"My goodness!" said Mrs. Little. "I'll tell
Mr. Little. He and some of the other men
will come over at once. They will help you."

147

Mr. Dawson's Surprise

It didn't take long for the men to get to Mr. Dawson's house.

"When did you see your wife last?" asked Mr. Little.

"Just before I started to Mr. Long's house," Mr. Dawson answered. "I was on my way home. I saw—did you hear a knock at the back door?"

"I think it's coming from the cellar," said Mr. Black.

All the men started down to the cellar. "Hello down there!" called Mr. Black.

"Hello!" came the answer. "Please let me out of here!"

"It's my wife!" cried Mr. Dawson.
"My dear! What are you doing down there?
Come on up. I have been looking
for you everywhere."

"I can't come up," said Mrs. Dawson.
"I can't get out. The door is locked."

"Oh, my word!" said Mr. Dawson.
"The key! It's hanging in a tall tree!"

"What on earth is it doing there?"
asked Mr. Black.

"Well, I tried to fly a kite," began
Mr. Dawson. "I dropped the string.
But I can't take time to tell you now.
It has something to do with Benjamin
Franklin. We must get that key right away."

The men started out to get the key.
They got a ladder and went to the tree.
It took them a long time to get the key.
They got it and Robert's kite, too.

Mrs. Dawson was very glad to get out
of the cellar. "I went down there to get
something," she said. "Then I couldn't
get out. I couldn't get the door open.
It was locked."

"My dear!" said Mr. Dawson. "Please
forgive me. I thought I had fixed the door
so you could open it. You must have been
scared to stay in the cellar."

"My goodness, no!" said Mrs. Dawson.
"I didn't like to stay there, but I got
the cellar cleaned."

That night after Mr. Dawson was in bed he asked, "My dear! Why do you think Benjamin Franklin tied a key to his kite string?"

"That's how he found out about electricity," answered Mrs. Dawson. "Why do you ask?"

But Mr. Dawson was going to sleep. He didn't even hear her.

Otherwise

There must be magic,
Otherwise,
How could day turn to night?

And how could sailboats,
Otherwise,
Go sailing out of sight?

And how could peanuts,
Otherwise,
Be covered up so tight?

Aileen Fisher

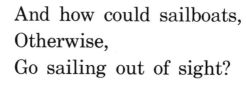

Rambling Richard

Once upon a time there was a man
who was called Rambling Richard.
He was called that because he liked to go
from town to town. He walked and walked
over the earth.

Rambling Richard liked to write.
Every day he tried to write a story.
Sometimes the story was real. Sometimes
it was make-believe. Sometimes it was funny.
Sometimes it was sad. But every day
he tried to write a story.

153

As Rambling Richard walked from place
to place he said to himself:

> I see what I see,
>   I go where I go.
> I do what I do,
>   I know what I know.
>
> Some people are funny,
>   Some people are sad.
> No one is all good,
>   No one is all bad.

One bright day Rambling Richard
was walking along. He came to the gates
of a town. He said to a man at the gates,
"What town is this?"

The man answered, "It is Grander Town.
I'm the Keeper of the Gates."

"Please let me go in," said Rambling
Richard. "I want to stay in the town today.
It's too hot to walk now."

"It's hot in Grander Town,"
said the Gate Keeper. "Twice as hot as
in any other town on earth."

"Is that so?" asked Rambling Richard.
"Are the nights hot, too?"

"No," the Gate Keeper answered.
"The nights are cold. Twice as cold
as they are in any other place on earth."

Rambling Richard didn't know
what to think of that, but he went on
into the town.

Rambling Richard met a man. "Friend,"
he said to the man, "I'm Rambling Richard.
Maybe you can tell me something.
All along the street I read words on cards.
They say, 'Bigger and Bigger, Taller and Taller,
Longer and Longer.' Why is this?"

The man looked sad. "In this town,"
he said, "the king tells us what to think.
He tells us what to do. He says we must have
twice as much of everything as others have.
He thinks that makes it a grand town."

"We have to work twice as hard
as others do," the man went on.
"We must always have twice as much
of everything in our town.
We must make two of everything.
Things must be twice as big. They
must be twice as tall and twice as long."

"My word!" said Rambling Richard.
"I have never been to a place like this."

"Come with me," said the man sadly.
"I will show you what happens."

The man showed Rambling Richard
a very high hill. Many men were working
there. They were making the hill twice
as high as any other hill.

In another place, men were making a hole.
It had to be twice as deep as any other hole.

"What's the good of all this?"
asked Rambling Richard. "Why should
the hill be twice as high? Why must
the hole be twice as deep?"

"I don't know," the man answered sadly.
"King Big-Wig says we must do it. Hundreds
of men fall into the deep hole."

"I'll stay long enough to write a story
for your king," said Richard. "Maybe that
will help."

"Maybe it will," said the sad man.

Twice Upon a Time

The next day Rambling Richard began
to write the story. Just as he finished it,
he heard a man shout, "Hello! Hello!"

He looked up and saw someone at his door.

"I come from King Big-Wig," said the man.
"He has learned about you. He wants you
to write a story for him. It must be twice
as long as any other story. It must
please the king twice as much, too."

"My story is ready," said Rambling
Richard. "Take me to your king."

The king sat on a very big chair
in a very big room. "Read me your story,"
he said.

Rambling Richard began to read:
"Once upon a time——"

The king jumped up from his chair.
"Stop!" said the king. "In some other town
you may begin a story with 'Once upon a time.'
But not in Grander Town. Here your story
must begin with 'Twice upon a time.' "

"May it please Your Highness,"
answered Rambling Richard. "I can't begin
a story that way."

"Take him away!" shouted King Big-Wig.
"No one says 'can't' to King Big-Wig.
Don't let him go until he writes the story."

That night Rambling Richard thought and thought about what to do. The next day the king sent for him.

"Do you have a story that begins, 'Twice upon a time'?" he asked.

"I can't write a story like that," answered Rambling Richard.

"Off with him!" shouted the king. "Don't give him anything to eat until he writes the story. I must have twice as much of everything."

Rambling Richard said, "Your Highness! There is something of which you have only one."

"What's that?" asked the king.

"You have only one king," said Rambling Richard. "Why not two kings?"

No one said a word. Everyone looked
at the king. What would he say to this?

At last the king asked, "What was that?
Did you say two kings?"

"**Two kings**," said Rambling Richard.

The people heard what he said.
They looked scared.

The king turned white. "We can't have
two kings," he said.

"You say that you want twice as much
of everything. Then you should have
two kings," said Rambling Richard.

The king thought and thought. At last
he asked, "What can I do? I want to have
twice as much of everything. We just
can't have two kings. What can I do?"

"I will tell you," said Rambling Richard.
"Stop trying to have more and bigger things
than others have. A thing is not always better
just because there is more of it. The Keeper
of the Gate is taller than you. Do people
like him better than the king just because
of that?"

King Big-Wig thought about that.
At last he smiled. "You are right,"
he said to Rambling Richard. "From now on,
we will not try to make things twice as big,
or tall, or long. We will try
to make them better."

The people cried, "The king! The king!
Long live the king!" They began to laugh,
and dance, and shout.

163

The king heard Rambling Richard's story. "Stay with us always, Rambling Richard," he said. "You have been to many places. Why not stay in Grander Town?"

"Thank you, Your Highness," said Rambling Richard. "I must go. I want to see the cherry trees in the next town. I hear that they are very beautiful. I'll read one more story and then be on my way."

"If you must go, you must," said King Big-Wig. "I'll give you a sack of gold to take with you. Now begin the story."

It was a good story. The king thought it was a very good story. It began, "Once upon a time ——"

A Tiger in the Cherry Tree

High in the hills of faraway Japan
there was a little town. A cherry tree grew
in the town—a small blue-green cherry tree.
The children of the town loved
the little cherry tree. So did all the people.
The landlord in the town said,
"Our little tree is very beautiful.
Someday it will be the most beautiful tree
in all Japan."

165

One day the children of the town
came running. "Honorable Landlord!"
they cried. "There is an old man sitting
in our cherry tree!"

There was an old man in the little tree.
An old man—and something was with him.

"Who are you?" asked the landlord.

"I'm a man who makes magic," answered
the old man. "This is my tiger."

"Ho!" laughed the landlord, taking hold
of the animal's tail. "This is no tiger!"

Just then the animal made a big noise—
a big tiger noise.

"It **is** a tiger!" shouted the landlord,
letting go of its tail. "What's it doing
in our tree?"

The old man answered, "We must have
a place to stay. We can no longer work
in the circus. My tiger is not very brave,
and he doesn't really like the circus. I'm
too old to work in the circus any longer,
anyway. It is never very cold here. Please
let us live in your beautiful cherry tree."

The landlord didn't know what to say.

"Let him stay, Honorable One," said
the people of the town. "Please let him stay."

"Please let the tiger stay, too," said
the children. "We will take care of it."

"So be it," answered the landlord.

167

Time went by in the little town.
The children loved the tiger.
He learned to dance with the children
in the streets.

The old man sat under the cherry tree and
did magic things. The people of the little town
learned to love him, too. That is, all but one
of them did.

The landlord of the town didn't like
the old man or his tiger.

"That old man should not be sitting
under our beautiful tree," he said. "It doesn't
look right. As for that animal, it's always
eating our cherries. We must catch it
and put a stop to that!"

One day the landlord sent his men to catch the tiger. The old man was sitting under the cherry tree. He saw the men coming.

"Don't put a hand on my tiger," he said. "I'll turn each of you into a red-and-black puppy if you do!" He would have done it, too, but he forgot the magic words.

It is hard to catch a tiger—even one that is not very brave. The men tried and tried, but the tiger always got away. At last they tried once more and got the tiger! They put him into a cage.

The old man saw what had happened.
He got very red and angry. He was so angry
that he jumped up and down under the tree.
He said some magic words. By the time
he had finished saying them, he and the tiger
were gone. They just went away into the air.
They were nowhere to be seen.

"Good thing!" said the angry landlord.
"Now that tiger won't eat our cherries
anymore."

The Sad Tree

The children cried for the tiger.
The people of the town were very sad, too.
The little cherry tree began to droop.
The cherries fell from it like big red tears.

"Our tree is crying for the tiger. It wants the man who makes magic, too," they said.

They were right.

"Find the old man," cried the landlord. "His magic can save our little tree."

For seven days and eight nights the people looked for the old man. They couldn't find him or the tiger.

The little cherry tree drooped and
drooped. Its last cherry had fallen,
like a big red tear. The children were
in tears, too. Everyone in the town
was very sad, even the landlord.

"Where is the old man of magic?"
they cried. "He can't be at the circus.
He is too old."

"...and his tiger is not brave enough
for the circus," said the children.

Up popped the little old man!

"...but he is just right for the cherry
tree," he said.

"Please! Oh, please!"
said the honorable landlord. "Save our tree!"

"So be it," answered the little old man. "The tree will be saved." He smiled and said some magic words.

The drooping tree began to grow beautiful! Then up popped the tiger. The children laughed and danced.

The old man and the tiger were happy. They were glad to be in their tree home once more.

As for the little cherry tree, it grew and grew. For all I know, it may still be there. It may still grow high in the hills of faraway Japan.

Could It Have Been a Shadow?

What ran under the rosebush?
  What ran under the stone?
Could it have been a shadow,
  Running away alone?
Maybe a fairy's shadow,
  Slipping away at dawn
To guard a gleaming pot of gold
For a busy leprechaun.

Monica Shannon

The Ugly Duckling

Down by the water an old mother duck
sat and sat on her eggs. At last
one egg after another began to crack.

"Peep! Peep! Peep!" she heard.
Little baby ducklings began to pop out
of the eggs. Soon the ducklings came out
from under the mother duck
and looked around.

"Are you all out now?"
asked the mother duck. She got up and looked
into the nest. "No," she said, "I don't have
all of you yet. One egg is still here."

She sat down on the nest again.

The next day another duck
came by the nest. "Well, how goes it?"
she asked.

"One egg is taking a long time to hatch,"
said the mother duck. "The other ducklings
are all out, and they are beautiful."

"Let me see the egg that won't hatch,"
said the other duck. When she saw it,
she said, "I don't think it's a duck's egg.
Let it stay there. Go and help your other
children learn to swim."

"I'll sit on it a little longer,"
said the mother duck. "I have sat on it
this long. I can sit another day or two."

"Do as you like," said the other duck.

At last the big egg hatched. The duckling
that came out didn't look like the others.
He was not little and yellow. He was big,
and gray, and ugly.

"What a big duckling!" said the mother
duck. "How big he will be when he grows up!
Can he really be a duck? Well, I know how
to find out. I'll take the ducklings
to the water and see if he can swim."

The ugly duckling did swim. He could
swim better than any of the ducklings.

"Yes, he is my own duckling,"
said the mother duck. "He may not be
so good-looking, but see how he can swim!
Really, he doesn't look bad at all."

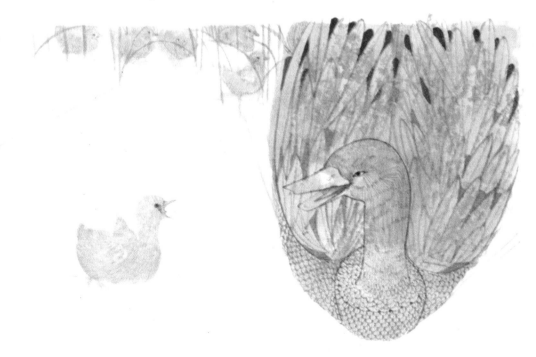

The mother duck took her children out
for a walk. One of the other ducks looked
at them. She said, "What a funny looking
duckling that one is! We don't want
him here." She flew at the ugly duckling
and bit him.

"Stop!" said his mother. "Let him alone!
He isn't hurting anyone."

Then she said to the ducklings, "Come on!
Let's not stay here."

They walked on and met a fat old duck.
"You have some good-looking children there—
all but one," he said. "He is really ugly.
It's too bad that you can't do something
to help his looks."

"That can't be done," said the mother duck.
"I don't think he looks so ugly. He's
a good duckling, and you should see him swim!
I think he will grow up to be all right."

Day after day things grew harder and
harder for the gray duckling. The chickens
and the ducks bit him. They made fun of him.
They talked about how ugly he looked.

At last the duckling thought to himself,
"I'm so ugly! I'll run away and stay
where no one can see me. It will be better
to be alone than to be here."

In the Far Woods

The duckling ran far away into the woods.
Only his mother was unhappy that he
had gone.

What a hard time the poor duckling had
after that! It would be too bad to tell
about it. He stayed in the woods all alone
for a long, long time.

He stayed away from everyone.
He didn't want anyone to see how ugly he was.

The duckling had to eat whatever
he could find in the woods.

The only fun he had was swimming
in the water. How he liked to swim!

The ugly duckling grew and grew,
as ducklings do.

When winter came, things grew harder
than ever for the ugly duckling. It was
very cold, and he could no longer swim.
He had a hard time finding enough to eat.

He thought the cold winter would never
be over. Winters were very long
where he lived.

He would stay in the woods and think
about spring. "When spring comes,
it will not be so cold," he thought.
"Then I can swim again."

All this time, the duckling grew
and grew. When spring did come at last,
the duckling had grown up. He had not seen
himself, so he didn't know that he was grown.
He didn't know how he looked now.

It was the first day of spring.
The ugly duckling was thinking of the water.
How he wanted to swim and float in it!

"I must go for a swim," he thought.
"The water is not so cold now."

When he got to the water,
he had a surprise. There on the water
floated some beautiful white birds. They
were the most beautiful birds the duckling
had ever seen. They were swans.

He looked and looked at the lovely swans.
He wanted to get close to them.

"I must go to them," he said. "When they
see how ugly I am, they will kill me. They
will not want me to come close to them.

"I'll go, anyway. I'll let them kill me. That will be better than to have the other ducks make fun of me."

The duckling began to swim. When he got close to the lovely swans, he bowed his head. "Kill me!" he said.

What did he see when he bowed his head? There in the water he saw himself, big, and white, and beautiful. He was no longer gray and ugly. He was a swan!

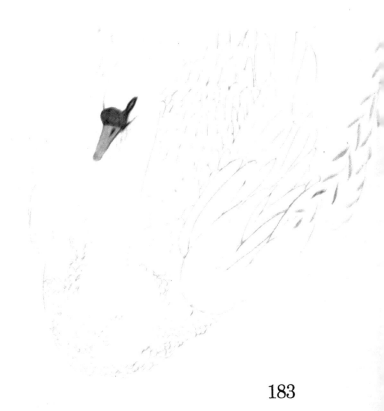

Some children came down to the lake
to bring the swans something to eat.

"There's a new one!"
cried one of the children.
"We haven't seen him before."

"Yes," said another. "He is the most
beautiful swan of all."

The swan thought of all his hard times
as an ugly duckling. Now he was
the most beautiful one of the lovely birds!

He held his head high and floated
across the water. The other swans
were happy to have him with them.

"I didn't know there could be
this much happiness!" he thought.

Why the Sea Is Salt

Once upon a time, long, long ago,
there were two brothers. One of the brothers
was very rich. The other was poor.

It happened one day that the poor brother
didn't have anything to eat. He went
to his brother and asked him for help.

Now, the rich brother didn't like to give
anything away. He had helped his brother
before. He was not glad to see him now.

"I'll give you something," he said.
"That is, if you say you will never ask me
for help again."

"All right," said the poor brother.
"I won't come back again."

He took the sack from his brother, and
thanked him very much. Then he looked
into the sack to see what was there.

The first thing he saw was a candle.
The next was bread. The last was some bacon.

The poor brother took the sack and
started home. On the way he saw an old man.

"Please!" said the old man. "Can you give
a poor old man something to eat?"

"I'm poor, myself," said the poor brother.
"But I'll give you some of the little I have."

He cut off some of the bread and gave it
to the old man. Then he handed him
the candle. "I'll give you some
of my bacon, too," he said.

"No," said the old man. "You have given me bread and a candle. That is enough. Now I want to do something for you. On the other side of the next hill, you will find a gate. It opens into a deep hole in the hillside. Open that gate and go inside."

"What will I find there?" asked the poor brother.

"You will find the little people who live in the hill," the old man answered. "They are called gnomes."

"The gnomes have a magic mill,"
said the old man. "It will grind out
almost anything they want. There is just
one thing it won't grind."

"What's that?" asked the poor brother.

"Bacon," the old man answered.
"When you get inside, the gnomes
will want your bacon. Don't sell it
for anything but the mill."

The poor brother did as he was told.
He soon came to the home of the gnomes
in the hillside. He found that the old man
was right. All the gnomes wanted his bacon.

"I'll sell it to you for that mill
over there," he said.

At first the gnomes said, "No."
They didn't want to let him have the mill.
The poor brother wouldn't sell them the bacon
without it. At last they gave him
the magic mill for the bacon.

First, the poor brother learned how
to use the mill. Then he took it home.

He put the mill down on the table.
His surprised wife looked on. "Grind bread,"
he said to the mill. "Grind bread, and meat,
and other good things to eat."

The magic mill began to grind.
Soon the table was almost covered
with bread, and meat, and cake. There were
other good things, too. The happy wife
could hardly believe what she saw.

The Mill Grinds

The poor brother said, "We will send
for our friends. They can help us eat
some of the good things our mill grinds.
Our happiness will make them glad. Let's ask
my brother, too."

When the rich brother came,
he was surprised at what he saw.
"Where did you get all this?" he asked.

The poor brother showed him the mill.
He showed him how it would grind out
anything he wanted.

The rich brother wanted that magic mill
more than anything. He tried to get
his brother to sell it to him.

At last the poor brother said he would sell
the mill. First he made it grind out
many good things. He made it grind enough
to last a long time. Then he let his brother
take the mill.

The rich brother was happy to get the mill.
He started home so fast that he didn't stop
to learn how to use it. He had seen how
his brother started it but he didn't know
how to stop it.

He said to his wife, "I'll get dinner."

He put the mill on the table. "Grind fish,"
he said. "Grind soup. Grind them in a hurry."

The mill began to grind. "Hurry!"
said the rich brother to his wife.
"Bring more bowls for soup and fish."
Soon every bowl and dish in the house
was filled. The mill kept on grinding.
Soup and fish covered everything and
began to run out the doors and windows.
The rich brother couldn't stop the mill.
He ran to the home of his brother.
"Take back your mill," he cried.
"Take it back at once! If it grinds
a little longer, the town will swim in soup!"
The poor brother stopped the mill.
He took it back to his home. He had it
grind gold and all kinds of fine things.
Soon he and his wife were very rich.
They had all the things they could ever use.

People everywhere heard about the mill.
One day a man who had a ship came to see it.
The man used his ship to go across the sea
for salt. He made money by selling the salt.

When the man saw the mill, he said,
"I need that. It could grind out salt for me.
Then I wouldn't have to go across the sea
to get salt. Please sell it to me."

The poor brother was poor no longer.
"All right," he said. "We don't need
anything more. You may have the mill."

The man took the mill to his ship. He
put it on a table and said, "Grind salt."

The mill began to grind.
Soon the man wanted to stop the mill,
but he didn't know how.

The mill went right on grinding.
Soon the ship had so much salt in it
that it was about to sink.

"What have I done?" cried the man.
"That mill will bring us no good!
The salt will sink the ship!"

"Let's throw the mill into the sea,"
cried his men. "Throw it in before we sink."

"All right," the man answered.

His men threw the mill into the sea.
It went down, down, into the water.
It was grinding salt as it went.
For all I know, it may be grinding still.

That is why the sea is salt. Anyway,
that's what some people say.

The Three Wishes

Once upon a time there was a woodcutter.
Every day he went into the woods
to cut down trees. He cut the trees into wood
to sell to others.

One day the woodcutter was at work
in the woods. He found a tree he could use,
and started to cut it down.

When he made the first cut in the tree,
he heard a cry. It was a soft cry,
like that of a little girl.

The woodcutter stopped to listen.
He heard someone say,
"Please, Mr. Woodcutter! Listen to me.
Don't cut this tree!"

"Who are you?" asked the woodcutter.
"Where are you? Why should I listen to you?"

Then the woodcutter saw a surprising thing.
Out of a crack in the tree came
a beautiful little fairy. She was dressed
all in shiny white and gold.

"Here I am," she said. "I'm a tree fairy,
and this tree is my home. Please don't cut
it down. It is the best tree that grows."

"No, good fairy," said the woodcutter.
"I won't cut your tree. I must cut wood
to sell, but I'll not cut your tree.
You may keep it always."

"Thank you," said the fairy. "I know
that people must have wood for their fires.
You must have wood to sell to them.
It is good of you to save my tree."

"Not at all," said the woodcutter.
"I'm glad to do it."

"Now let me do something to thank you
for your kindness," said the fairy. "You
and your wife may have three wishes.
Wish anything you like, and it will happen.
Use the wishes well. They can bring you
many good things."

Before the woodcutter could say
another word, the fairy was gone.

197

Making the Wishes

The woodcutter wanted to tell his wife about the fairy, but he made himself stay and finish his work. "I'm a long way from home," he thought. "I mustn't go back without something to show for my work."

So the woodcutter cut wood all day long. Then he started home. By that time he was very hungry.

As soon as he got home, he told his wife about the fairy and the three wishes. Then he said, "Let's eat now. I'm hungry!"

"Oh, no!" she said. "Not now. It will be a long time before anything is ready. Let's think about the three wishes. What are we going to wish?"

The hungry woodcutter said, "I want to eat first. All I can think about is something to eat. I wish I had a big long sausage ready to eat right now."

The words were hardly said before the sausage was there! It was big and brown and hot, ready to eat.

"See what you have done!" cried the woodcutter's wife. "You have used one of our wishes!"

"I forgot," said the woodcutter. He looked very sad. "I was so hungry I forgot about the wishes."

"You forgot!" cried his angry wife. "That was a fine thing to do! All you got with that wish was one sausage! Ha! I wish the sausage were on the end of your nose!"

Another wish was gone! Right on the end
of the woodcutter's nose was the big
brown sausage!

"Oh, what have I done!" cried his wife.

The woodcutter and his wife tried to pull
the sausage off his nose. They tried
and tried, but they couldn't pull it off.

They sat down to think what to do.

"We have just one wish now,"
said the woodcutter. "We must use it well."

"Yes," said his wife. "Let's wish
for a big sack of gold. Then we will be rich.
We can use the gold to get all the things
we need. We can even cover the sausage
with gold. Then it won't look so ugly."

200

"No," said the woodcutter. "I don't want this thing on the end of my nose.
I don't want it covered with gold.
I'll never be happy again as long
as it's there. We can't pull it off."

"Then we must wish it off," said his wife.
"Things will be just as they were before we got
the three wishes. We were happy then."

"That's right," said the woodcutter.
"So we were."

They used their last wish to get the sausage
off the woodcutter's nose. They didn't have
a sack of gold, but they did have
a fine, big sausage!

201

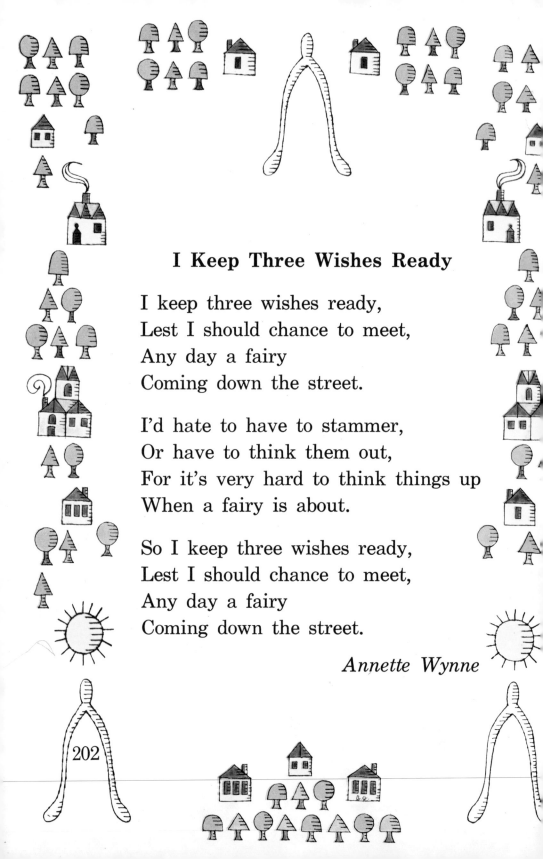

I Keep Three Wishes Ready

I keep three wishes ready,
Lest I should chance to meet,
Any day a fairy
Coming down the street.

I'd hate to have to stammer,
Or have to think them out,
For it's very hard to think things up
When a fairy is about.

So I keep three wishes ready,
Lest I should chance to meet,
Any day a fairy
Coming down the street.

Annette Wynne

202

Scat!   Scitten!

Even though
  a cat has a kitten,
  not a rat has a ritten,
  not a bat has a bitten,
  not a gnat has a gnitten,
  not a sprat has a spritten.
That is that—that is thitten.

David McCord

Thinking of Others

Three Cousins

"This wagon won't go," said Pam.

"Let me help you," said her grandmother.
"That wagon is too old to use any longer.
Looks as if I'll just have to get a new one."

Pam had come to stay with her
grandmother and grandfather for six days.
They were at their little summer place
by the sea. They stayed there every summer
and Pam liked to go there to see them.

This summer, it was going to be
more fun than ever at Grandmother's.
Two of Pam's cousins were coming.

Pam had never seen her cousins. Andrea,
the older one, lived in a faraway town.
She was nine. Kate was not as old as Pam.
She was seven. Kate lived on a farm.
It was far away, too.

Pam and her grandmother fixed the wagon
so it would go. When they got home,
Pam heard her grandfather calling her.
She ran to see what he wanted.
She saw him in the door of his workshop.

"Come out here, Pam," he said.
"I have something to show you."

They went inside the workshop. He showed
her a new wagon. It was painted pink!

"I made it for your grandmother's
birthday," said Pam's grandfather.
"You mustn't tell."

"Oh, no!" said Pam. "I won't tell.
She needs a new wagon. We could hardly
get home with that old one today."

"Pam!" Now it was Grandmother calling.

"It's time to go to the boat,"
said her grandmother. "Time for your cousins
to come."

"Oh, good!" cried Pam. "I'm so glad
Kate and Andrea are coming. I'll have
someone to play with."

When Andrea and Kate got off the boat, Pam thought, "They don't look the same at all."

Andrea was tall, and looked very grown up for a girl of nine. Kate was smaller. She had a doll in one hand.

Andrea said, "Kate has a doll with her. Think of that! Why, I stopped playing with dolls a long time ago. Kate is silly."

"Andrea thinks I'm a baby!" said Kate, looking angry. "She thinks she's grown up!"

Pam didn't know what to say.

All that day Pam tried to keep her cousins happy. Things didn't work out very well. They never wanted to do the same things. Andrea wanted to swim, but Kate didn't know how.

Kate sat near the water and played
with her doll. Andrea went swimming.
Pam played in the water where she could
be near both of them. That was not much fun.

The next day was just as bad.

The girls' grandfather said,
"Let's all go fishing."

Andrea and Kate didn't want to go.

"All right," said their grandmother.
"You girls can stay here and play. I'll go
with Grandfather. We will fish near the house
so you can call us if you need us."

Grandmother didn't know what was going
to happen! She wouldn't have gone fishing
if she had known.

The Pink Wagon

Kate saw Bobby, the little boy next door.
She went to play with him.

Andrea played by herself.

Pam almost wished her cousins hadn't
come. She tried to think of something
they could do together. She thought
of the wagon.

"Kate! Andrea!" she called. "Want to see
a surprise?"

They both came to see what it was.
Pam told them about the wagon.
"I'll show it to you," she said.

When Andrea saw the pink wagon
she said, "I never saw a **pink** wagon before!"

"Grandma likes pink," Pam said.

Kate said, "I like the wagon!"

"So do I," said Andrea. "Let's try it."

"Maybe we shouldn't," said Kate.
"It's to be a surprise."

"Don't be silly," said Andrea.
"Grandma can't see us on the walk."

Andrea began to pull the wagon out.

"Maybe it will be all right," said Pam.
"We will just pull it up and down the walk."

Bobby's mother saw the girls
with the wagon. She thought they
were going to the store.

"Please take some bottles back to the store
for me," she said. "I have four more inside.
The man at the store will give you
some money for them. You can have it
to use as you like."

She put six bottles into the new wagon.

"Each of us can take two bottles
to the store," said Pam.

"No," said Andrea. "We will take them
in the new wagon."

Pam didn't want to say no to Andrea.
"All right," she said, but she
didn't feel right about it.

"Let's take Bobby," said Kate.
"He will love riding in the pink wagon."

Kate ran inside to ask Bobby's mother
about it. She soon came back with Bobby.

"Don't take **him**!" said Andrea.
"I'm not going if he goes."

"We **will** take him!" cried Kate.
"It's not going to hurt you if he goes."

Pam said, "Oh, come on, Andrea!"

"No!" cried Andrea. "I'll play by myself.
I'll think up something that's fun."

Before they knew it, the three girls
were quarreling.

At last Kate and Pam started off.
Bobby and the bottles were in the wagon.
Andrea didn't go.

Pam and Kate got to the boat dock
and took Bobby out of the wagon. Each girl
took three bottles. Bobby and the girls
went inside the store.

They left the wagon on the boat dock.

Many people were in the store.
The girls had to wait for their turn.

Bobby didn't like to wait. He went
to the window and looked out at the water.

After a long time, their turn came.
The man took the bottles and gave Pam
the money for them.

Just then they heard Bobby crying.
He was still looking out the store window.
He was crying and saying, "Wawa! Wawa!"

"Come on, Bobby," said Pam, taking him
by the hand. "We are ready to go."

He went with her, but kept on saying,
"Wawa! Wawa!"

The girls went out to the dock
where they had left the wagon.

"Kate!" cried Pam. "Where is the wagon?"

It was gone!

"Maybe Andrea took it," said Kate.

The two girls took Bobby home as fast
as he could go. Then they found Andrea.

Where Is the Wagon?

"All right, Andrea!" said Pam.
"What did you do with the wagon?"

"The wagon?" asked Andrea. Her eyes
grew big with surprise.

"It's gone," Kate answered.
"Did you take it?"

"No!" shouted Andrea. She looked
so angry that the other girls knew
she didn't take it. "If it's gone,
we must find it," she said. "We
must find it before Grandpa gets back."

The three girls looked everywhere.
They couldn't find the wagon.

At last they sat down to think what to do.

216

"We can't find the wagon," said Andrea. "We should do something to make Grandma happy on her birthday. I could make a ready-mix cake for her."

"I could put pink candles on it," said Kate. "The store sells them."

"I think Bobby's mother will let you make it at her house," said Pam. "Then it can be a surprise. The money we got for the bottles will help get the things."

Pam thought it was smart of Andrea to think of the cake. Maybe it would make Grandma feel better.

Just then Pam thought of something.

She said, "At the store, Bobby kept saying, 'Wawa! Wawa! Wawa!' Maybe he was trying to tell us that the wagon was in the water."

"How could it be?" asked Andrea.
She **didn't** say, "Don't be silly."

"We left it on the dock," Pam answered.
"Maybe it went into the water. Bobby was
at the window, so maybe he saw it fall in."

Kate said, "If it's in the water,
Andrea can get it. She's a good swimmer."

"Let's see if it's there," said Andrea.

The girls ran to the dock. There was
the wagon, in the water near the dock.

"I'm going to get it," said Andrea.
"I can swim under water."

"No!" said Pam. "The water is too deep.
Grandma wouldn't like it. Some big boys
are swimming out there. Let's ask them
to get it."

The big boys got the wagon
out of the water. They put it on the dock.

The girls put the wagon back
into the workshop. Just then
their grandfather came.

When he saw the dirty wagon, he looked
surprised and angry. "How did that wagon
get all wet and dirty?" he asked.

The girls told him what had happened.
Their grandfather saw that they felt
very unhappy about it.

"Well," he said, "I think you will be
more careful next time. The wagon isn't hurt.
It's just dirty. You girls can clean it."

219

The girls worked hard. Soon the wagon began to look pink and shiny again.

Andrea said, "Just wait until we tell Grandma all about this! We will tell her how smart Pam was. Pam thought of what Bobby was trying to say."

Pam's ears got red. She liked to have Andrea say she was smart. She looked at her cousins. The three of them were friends now.

Pam laughed. "Do you know?" she said. "Before you came I didn't know what it was like to have a cousin!"

"A cousin is a very fine thing to have!" said Kate.

"Yes!" said Andrea. "That's right!"

The three girls laughed together just because they were happy.

The Boy Called Booie

Booie Baker wanted to be a ball player
someday. He could run very fast—
faster than any other boy on his street.
He could catch all right, too. But he just
couldn't hit the ball.

Booie thought that he was going to be
a ball player anyway. He thought so
until one day when his friend Butch
had a birthday. Butch was eight that day.
It was a Saturday.

That morning Booie heard Butch
at the back door. "Come on in," he called.
Butch came in, looking very happy.

"Look!" he yelled. "Look at the ball
and bat my dad gave me!"

"How is that for a neat bat?" he asked.
Then he said, "Hurry up, Booie.
Let's go try them out."

"All right," said Booie. The two boys
went out together.

As soon as they got outside, they saw
four other boys. All the boys lived
on their street. They were talking together.

A new boy was with them. He was
a tall, red-headed boy. Booie and Butch
didn't know him. He had just come to live
in a new house. The house was right
across the street from Booie's home.

The boys saw Butch's new ball and bat.
They all came across the street to look
at them. The new boy came, too.

"Let's play ball," said the red-headed boy.
"Where do you play?"

Butch answered, "Over at the playground.
We will show you, Red."

Booie wished that Butch could pitch to him
before they played with the red-headed boy.
Then maybe he could hit better when his
turn came. There was no time for that now,
so he went on with the other boys.

When it was Red's turn at bat,
he hit the ball hard. Booie had to run
to the other end of the playground to get it.
Booie wished that he could hit like that.
Oh, how he wished it! He had never wished
for anything so much before.

In no time at all it was Booie's turn.
He swung the bat once or twice
the way the big boys always did.

"Ready?" asked Red, who was pitching.

"Yes," Booie answered.

Red threw the ball fast and straight.

Booie swung hard—and missed.

"It feels as if I had something
in my eye," said Booie. "If that
hadn't happened, maybe I would have——"

Red was getting ready for the next pitch.

He threw another fast ball.

Booie missed again.

"Why can't you hit the ball?" Red asked.
"I'm throwing them right to you."

"But——" Booie began.

"No ifs, ands, or buts!" Red said.
"One more strike and you are out."

Once more Red pitched the ball straight.
Once more Booie swung hard and missed.
Three strikes and out!

"My little sister can hit a ball
better than you can!" Red said.
"What did you say your name is?"

"Booie," said Booie.

Red turned to the other boys and said,
"Boy! He sure hits like someone
who would be called Booie."

Booie didn't say anything more.
He was so angry he wanted to cry or fight,
but he didn't. He handed the bat to Butch.

"Here. I don't want to play," he said.

Booie felt very unhappy. He didn't know
that something would happen to make things
better for him.

Something New

When Booie got home, he went straight
to his mother.

"Mother," he said. "Why do you
call me Booie? That's not my name."

"Oh!" said his mother, "didn't I tell you
about that? When you were a baby,
your sister was not old enough to talk
very well. When she tried to say, 'Baby,'
she always said 'Booie.' So we began
calling you Booie. Then other people did, too."

"It's not my name," said Booie.
"My name is Dick, like Father's name."

Just then his father came home.

Mr. Baker said, "Hi, Booie! You and I
are going on a trip next Saturday."

"Where?" asked Booie.

"To see Dr. Stone," his father said.
"We had a letter from your school.
We were asked to see a doctor about your eyes.
After we see him, we will have something good
to eat. Maybe we will look around in the stores
before we come home."

"My eyes are all right," Booie said.
"I don't need to see a doctor about them.
But I'm glad we are going, because I like
to eat out."

When the next Saturday came, Dr. Stone
put big eyeglasses on Booie. He asked him
to read some letters. They were on the wall
at the far end of the room. Dr. Stone put
one glass after another in the big eyeglasses.
He kept asking Booie which one was best.

All at once something happened. As he put
one glass in place, Booie saw very well.
He saw better than he had ever seen before.
He could read every letter on the wall.

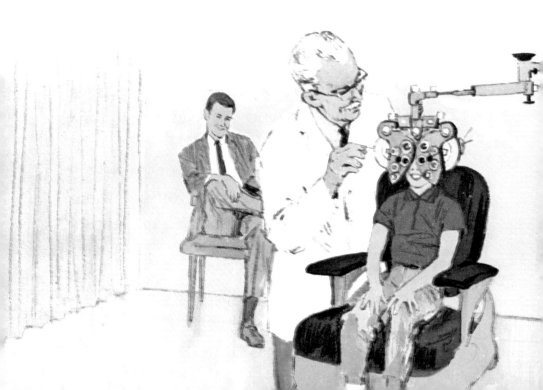

"Say!" Booie cried in surprise. "I can see fine now!"

"That's right! You can." Dr. Stone laughed and turned to Booie's father. "He just needs glasses. When he gets them, he'll be all right."

"Glasses?" said Booie. "Not eyeglasses!"

"That's right," said Dr. Stone.

"I don't want any old eyeglasses!" cried Booie.

"You will like them after you get them," said Mr. Baker. "Thank Dr. Stone, and let's go."

228

Booie got his glasses the next Saturday.
He was surprised at how well he could see
when he wore them.

He saw a bird's nest in the tree
outside his bedroom window. He had never
seen it before. He saw a little green ring
in the paper on the wall. All that day
and the next he wore the glasses
and saw new things. He liked that.

"But I don't want to wear the glasses
to school," he thought to himself.
"I'm afraid the children will laugh at me."

It made Booie very unhappy to think
about wearing them.

What Happened at School?

Booie was far from happy when he wore his glasses to school. He waited for someone to laugh at the new glasses. No one seemed to see that he was wearing eyeglasses.

Booie could see everything just fine. The words seemed to pop out at him. Soon he found that he was doing his work better and faster than ever before.

The same thing happened when the children went outdoors to play. Things seemed so bright and close. Booie could catch a ball better, too.

Butch took his new ball and bat to the playground. Red and the other boys didn't have a bat and ball.

Red said, "Want to play with us, Butch?"

Butch looked at Booie. "Sure, if Booie can play, too," he said. "It's our ball and bat, so our side is up at bat first."

Booie was the first man up at bat. Red was pitching.

Booie found that he could see Red very well. He could see him better than he had ever seen a pitcher before.

"Ready?" Red asked.

"Sure," said Booie.

Red pitched the ball. Booie could see it come straight to him. He swung the bat. The bat hit the ball hard. It went high over Red's head, and came down at the far end of the playground.

By this time Booie was running as fast
as he could run.

"I hit it that time, for sure!" he thought.

"Oh, boy!" yelled Red. "It's a home run!"

And that is just what it was!

Butch and some of the other boys
ran over to Booie. Butch began to hit him
on the back. "I knew you could do it!
Good old Booie!"

"What happened to you?" yelled Red.
"That was a fine hit!"

Booie looked across the playground
at Red. He seemed so close, and Booie
could see how friendly he looked.

Just then they heard the bell ring. Booie walked back to the school with Butch and Red. As they walked, he thought of something.

"My right name is Dick," he said. "From now on you can call me Dick."

"But we all call you Booie," said Butch. "Why do we have to call you Dick?"

"No ifs, ands, or buts!" said Booie. "Just call me Dick from now on. All right with you?"

"Sure," said Red.

Butch said, "Right with me."

Back in the schoolroom, Booie wrote his name on his paper. *Booie Baker,* he wrote. Then he quickly rubbed off the word *Booie.* *Dick Baker,* he wrote. It looked fine!

Home to Me Is Not a House

Home to me is not a house
Filled with family faces;
Home is where I slide in free
By rounding all the bases.

A tie to me is not
Clothing like a hat;
It means the game is even up
And I wish I were at bat.

Eve Merriam

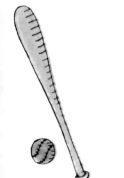

The Snowstorm

"Oh, Mother!" said Betsy. "There's
a little girl in the other bed in my room.
I have never seen her before!"

Before her mother could answer,
Star came running into the room.

"Mother!" she cried. "A little boy
is hanging upside down out of the top
of my bed!"

Their mother laughed.

235

"Yes," she said. "They are Neddie
and Susan. Their mother is here, too.
They came home with your father last night.
Their car had stopped in the snowstorm,
and they couldn't get home. Father's car
stopped, too. They all had to walk a long way
to get here."

"Will they go home this morning?"
asked Betsy.

"They can't go until this bad storm
is over," her mother answered. "They can't
even telephone home. All the telephone wires
are down. We must be very kind to Neddie
and Susan and their mother."

236

"Oh, we will!" said Betsy. "We like having them here. It won't be so bad to stay inside if we have someone to play with us. Come on, Star. Let's go see Neddie and Susan."

The snowstorm kept on for days. The children played everything they knew how to play. They liked to play together, but it was hard to stay inside so long. They couldn't even look at TV. There was no electricity to run it.

One morning Neddie looked out and said, "Still storming! We can't go out today." Then he turned to Betsy. "What can we do now?" he asked.

"Let me think," said Betsy. "Oh, I know! Maybe we can pop some popcorn. We have a new popper."

"That would be fun," said Neddie.
"Then may we eat it?"

"Oh, yes," Betsy answered.

"How I love popcorn!" said Susan.

"We have a big can of popcorn,"
said Betsy. "Let's go get it and the popper.
We can bring them in here and pop the corn
by the fire."

They all went to the kitchen. Betsy got
the things together. "Here, Neddie," she said.
"You take this can of corn. I'll take
the popper and Susan may take
a glass bowl. Can you take the popcorn
without dropping it, Neddie?"

"I never drop anything," said Neddie.

They took the things to the living room.

Susan looked at the popper Betsy had
in her hands. "Betsy!" she said. "That popper
is run by electricity! We can't use it."

Neddie never could tell how it happened,
but just then he tripped and fell. He dropped
the can and the top came off. Popcorn flew
all over the room. It was everywhere.

"Oh!" cried Neddie. "I tripped and
look what happened."

"What will we do now?" asked Star.

The Popcorn

"Come on!" said Betsy. "We have
to pick up this corn. We don't have another
can of popcorn."

"Are we going to eat popcorn that's been
on the floor?" asked Susan.

"We can wash it," Betsy answered.

"That's right," said Susan.
"We can wash it. Come on, all of you.
Help us pick it up."

The children went to work. It took them
a long time to pick up all the popcorn.
Then they took the corn to the kitchen,
and Betsy washed it.

"That was hard work," said Neddie, "and
now we can't have any popcorn. The popper
won't work."

"The corn is all wet," said Susan.
"It wouldn't pop anyway. It's too wet."

Betsy said, "I know what! We can put
the corn into pans and dry it in the oven.
It doesn't run with electricity."

All the children thought that was
just the thing to do. Betsy put the corn
into two big pans and put them into the oven.
"It may take the corn a long time to dry,"
she said.

"Read us a story, Betsy," said Star.
"You can read it while we wait."

"All right," Betsy answered.

They all went back into the living room
and sat by the fire. Betsy began to read.
Soon the children were in the land
of make-believe. There by the fire,
all other things were forgotten—
the snowstorm, the corn popper,
and the corn in the oven.

After a while the children's mothers
came into the living room. "I smell
something good," said Betsy's mother.
"It smells like popcorn."

Popcorn! That word made Betsy think
of something. She came back from the land
of make-believe in a hurry. She ran
to the kitchen. The others ran after her.

Betsy opened the oven door. There was
a blast of something white. It was
popped corn. It flew out of the open door.
It flew all over Betsy and all over the floor.

"Betsy!" cried her mother. "Why did you
put all that popcorn in the oven?"

"I didn't know it was going to pop,"
said Betsy. "I was trying to dry it."

"Dry it?" asked her mother. "Why did you
have to dry it?"

"It was so wet," Betsy answered.

"Wet!" said her mother. "How did it
get wet?"

"We had to wash it," said Betsy.

"But why were you washing popcorn?"
asked her mother.

"Neddie tripped, and it fell on the floor,"
Betsy answered.

"Well!" said her mother. "I know
one thing—we must get all that popcorn
out of the oven."

"That's a lot of popcorn," said Neddie.
"It smells good. I just love popcorn."

"I'm glad you do," said Betsy's mother.
"Every bowl and pan in this kitchen
is going to be filled with popcorn.
You will be eating popcorn for a long time."

The Hot-Weather Mix-Up

(A Play)

The People in the Play

GRANDPA WELLMAN

JIM JONES   MRS. JONES

PENNY WATERS   MRS. WATERS

BILLY ROBERTS   MRS. ROBERTS

SOME OTHER BOYS AND GIRLS

Scene 1

Time: A summer morning

Place: Near GRANDPA WELLMAN'S house.
He is sitting under a tree. A table
with a glass of water on it is near him.

GRANDPA. What weather! Going to be ninety-five today.

JIM JONES (*Running down the street, sees* GRANDPA). Hi, Grandpa.

GRANDPA. Stop running, Jim.
Going to be ninety-five today.

JIM. That's fine. *(Runs off)*

GRANDPA (*Picks up glass of water, takes a little of it*). Boys just don't feel the hot weather. It makes me hot just to see Jim run. *(Puts the glass down as* PENNY WATERS *comes in playing with a ball)* Going to be ninety-five today, Penny.

PENNY (*Playing with her ball*). Oh!
I didn't know that, Grandpa. *(Runs off)*

BILLY ROBERTS *(Comes along on his skates. Stops near walk)*. Hi, Grandpa!

GRANDPA. This weather is too hot for skating, Billy. Going to be ninety-five today.

BILLY. Say, that's something! *(Skates quickly away)*

GRANDPA *(Gets up from his chair)*. I just can't look at the children playing any longer. It makes me feel too hot. I'll go into the house and go to sleep.

Scene 2

Time: Later on the same day

Place: Near GRANDPA WELLMAN'S house, as in the first scene. MRS. JONES and MRS. WATERS are putting a small table under the tree. MRS. ROBERTS comes in with a cake in her hands. After her come JIM, PENNY, BILLY, and some other boys and girls. JIM and BILLY are bringing paper cups of ice cream.

ALL *(As they get near the table)*. Surprise!
 Surprise!
PENNY· Come out, Grandpa. We have a big
 surprise for you.
GRANDPA *(Comes out of the house. Goes over
 to table and looks at the cake)*. What's
 all the noise? What's going on here?
ALL CHILDREN. Happy birthday, Grandpa.
THREE MOTHERS. Happy birthday, Grandpa.
MRS. WATERS. We hear you are ninety-five
 today. We made a cake for you.
GRANDPA *(Looks surprised)*. What's that?
 What's that? Who says I'm ninety-five?
 I'm not nearly that old, and this isn't
 my birthday. I had my birthday in May!
PENNY. But you told us you were going to be
 ninety-five today!

GRANDPA *(Looks surprised)*. You have
things mixed up. I was talking about
the temperature! That's what was going
to be ninety-five. Not me!

MRS. ROBERTS. The temperature? It may be
ninety-five later today, but it's not
quite that hot yet.

MRS. JONES. Well, let's go on with our surprise
for Grandpa even if he isn't ninety-five.

ALL CHILDREN *(Run to table)*. Yes, yes!

JIM *(Pulls out chair)*. Sit here, Grandpa.

MRS. WATERS *(Cuts cake and gives some of it
to GRANDPA)*. Here, Grandpa Wellman.
Have some of your birthday cake.

GRANDPA. There's something about the fun
we are having that makes me forget
the hot weather.

Friends

In the morning bright and cool,
That's the time I start for school.

Halfway there, or just about,
Freddie, my best friend, comes out.

If he is a little late,
Then I whistle at his gate.

When we play a choosing game,
Freddie always calls my name.

We are friends, and so we share
Everything, most everywhere.

May Justus

Quibble

U can be seen without a Q
But Q must always go with U.

I think it's queer
And not quite right.

So here is a Q all on its own.
Come on, Q. Stand up alone.
U keep out.

Alas, poor Q feels q_ivery, q_avery,
Q–ietly sick . . .

Hurry back, U,
To the rescue—quick!

Eve Merriam

Word List for *ENCHANTED GATES*

The words introduced in ENCHANTED GATES, Second Reader, Book 1, are listed below. They are of three types:

Developmental (boldface type): Words which the authors anticipate most pupils will not be able to identify independently. They are words that will be used in the development of word-analysis skills, or words that should be taught as wholes because they are unsuited to analysis.

Skills Practice (regular type): Words which many pupils will be able to identify with the word-analysis skills that they have developed by that time, but for which other pupils will require more supervised skills practice.

Assumed (*italics*): Words which pupils are expected to identify independently with skills that have become well established. In this book the list of assumed words appears on pages 255-256.

For a complete description of categories, see the Teacher's Annotated Edition and Guide to accompany ENCHANTED GATES.

10.
11.
12. Andy
    Hardy
    Kay
    Mrs.
13. **door**
14. **getting**

---

15. **I'll**
16. hanging
    pants
17. fix
18. holes
    sack

---

19. feet
    stopped
20.
21.
22. **petted**
23. **happen**
24. its

---

25. **Jenny**
    outside
    wobbly
26. two-wheeler
27. **skates**

---

28. **careful**
    our

29. foot
    pedal
    riding
30. **long**

---

31. coming
    goes
    keep
    skating
32.
33. held
34. **push**
35.

36.
37.
38.

---

39. **ears**
    hound-pup
40. **dinner**
41. **every**
    tied
42. **unhappy**
43. dish
    yourself

---

44. **bark**
    oldest
    shiny
45. **secret**
46. **small**

47. **because**
    bigger
    Saturday
48.

---

49. **money**
    pennies
    Timmy
50. Dick
51. bank
52. fill
    pint
    top

---

53. **teacher**
54. **librarian**
    library
    would
55. **answer**
    some
    until

56.
57.
58. **hundred**
59. penny
60. **sixty-nine**

---

61. Danny
    dollars
    finish
62. think

what's
63. **eight**
    I'm
    taking
64. Frank
    seven
    Kakai
65. he's
66. should

67.
68.
69.

70.
71.
72. Betty
    surprise
73. **always**
    Chet
74. cookbook
75. **opened**
    sight

---

76. read
77. beat
    bowl
    eggs
78. **sugar**
79.
80. cried
    gave

81. **important**
salt
82.

83. ago
Franklin
real
84. use
85. blow
86. **much**
87.

88. across
water
89. kite
string
90. **Benjamin**
electricity
magic
91. **experiment**
rubbed
silk

92. **key**
lightning
93. **spark**
wire
94.

95. **David**
most
wish
96. **hobby**
Sue
97. page
really
smiled
98. vote
99. chicken
crack
vinegar

100. taken
turns
101. cover
shish
102. bend
soft
103.

104. need

105. **Maria**
Patrick
106. cars
107.
108.
109. **which**

110. **learn**
room
111. stories
112. found
113. **tomorrow**
114. **address**
115. **space**

116. choose
117. **only**
tail
wagger
118. **kept**
shop
119. spot
120. wagged
121.

122.

123. **Miss**
monkey
124.
125. **Army**
Navy
126. **afraid**
smallest
127.
128.

129. **Able**
130. **alive**
ships
131. **pulled**
132. glad
gone
133.

134.
135.

136.
137.
138. cellar
clean
Dawson
fly
Shaw
139. **forgotten**
lock
Robert
140.
141.
142. **dropped**
143. dear
thought

144. **knock**
wife
145. funny
telephone
146. **once**
147. **goodness**

148. started
149. **been**
150.
151. even

152.

153. Rambling
Richard
town
154. gates
place
155. Grander
twice
156.
157. sadly
158.

159. shout
160. begin
chair
Highness
161.

162.
163. better
dance
164. **beautiful**
cherry

165. grew
Japan
landlord
tiger
166. **animal**
Honorable
167. **circus**
168. under
169. **done**
170. angry

171. droop
172. fallen
popped
173. grow
still

174.

175. **duckling**
nest
peep
ugly
176. hatch
swim
177.
178. alone
179.

180. **poor**
woods
181. grown
spring
winter
182. lovely
swans
183. bowed
head
184. **happiness**

185. rich
sea

186. **bacon**
bread
candle
187. **gnomes**
188. almost
grind
189. **believe**
table

190.
191. fast
soup
192. **windows**
193.
194. sink
threw
throw

---

195. woodcutter
196. fairy
listen
197. fires
kindness

---

198. hungry
199. Ha
sausage
200.
201.

202.
203.

204.
205.
206. **cousins**
summer
wagon
207. **Andrea**
208.
209. silly
210. known

---

211. **Bobby**
Grandma
212. **bottles**
store
213. feel
214. dock
left
wait
215. wawa

---

216. **eyes**
217. **ready-mix**
smart
218.
219. dirty
220.

---

221. **Booie**
Butch
222.
223. pitch
playground
224. **straight**
strike
swung
225. **sure**

---

226. **Dr.**
Stone
trip
227. **eyeglasses**
228.
229. **paper**
wear
wore

---

230. seemed
231.
232.
233. **quickly**
wrote

234.

---

235. **snowstorm**

236. **Neddie**
Susan
237. popcorn
popper
238. dropping
kitchen
239.

---

240. floor
wash
241. dry
oven
while
242. smell
243.
244.

---

245. **scene**
246. **ninety-five**
247. cream
ice
later
248.
249. quite
temperature

250.
251.

Assumed Words

The words below are grouped by stories in which they appear. These are words which pupils are expected to identify independently with skills that have become well established. Suggestions for using this list in meeting individual or group needs will be found in many lesson plans throughout the *Guide* that accompanies this book.

Pages 10-24
Hardy's
helped
way
hole
running
packages
putting
Andy's

Pages 25-35
happened
maybe
today
it's
Jenny's
rains
Pete
sidewalk
pedals
side
wheeled
helping
skate
happens
without
harder
round

Pages 39-48
hound-pup's
pup
rabbits
ack
jay
doghouse
ear
tie
toy
laughing
times
barked
himself
smaller
barking

eating
hound

Pages 49-60
ten
Timmy's
hand
pocketbook
Nan
jar
keeps
answered
banker
finds
myself
Saturdays
filled

Pages 61-66
Sam
thinking
Green's
Sam's
fishing
Frank's

Pages 72-82
Hall
everything
Joy
sometimes
staying
isn't
than
beater
egg
cup
here's
puts
anyway
making
bite
hers
pleased
well
another

Pages 83-94
Pat
any
sell
everyone
inside
seated
asking
finding
ways
made
experiments
jars
used
Franklin's
helper
bell
ring
answers

Pages 95-104
wishing
plan
kinds
plans
reading
telling
rubber
wishbone
David's
note
turn
dee
finished
turned
handed
hands
opening
votes
bones
cracks

Pages 105-121
Patrick's
someone

somewhere
teach
Black's
color
sleeps
car
there's
policeman's
children's
never
whatever
card
yet
bring
outer
learned
ones
saying
colors
named
holding
pick
picked

Pages 123-133
Baker
sent
monkeys
needs
planned
send
cages
West
being
longer
upside
cone
nine
nose
far
fixed
open
ship
doctors
astronauts